CALCULUS

BEING A VERY-SIMI
THOSE BEAUTIFUL I
WHICH ARE GENERALLY CALLED BY THE
TERRIFYING NAMES OF THE

DIFFERENTIAL CALCULUS

AND THE

INTEGRAL CALCULUS

SILVANUS P. THOMPSON, F.R.S.

THIRD EDITION

M

First Edition 1910.
Reprinted 1911 (twice), 1912, 1913.
Second Edition 1914.
Reprinted 1915, 1917; with corrections 1918 (twice).
Revised and enlarged, 1919.
Reprinted 1920, 1921, 1922, 1924, 1927, 1931, 1936, 1940, 1942, 1943.
Third Edition 1946
Reprinted 1948, 1950, 1952, 1957, 1961, 1965, 1969, 1971, 1974, 1976

Published by
THE MACMILLAN PRESS LTD
London and Basingstoke
Associated companies in New York Dublin
Melbourne Johannesburg and Madras

ISBN 0 333 00007 2 (hard cover)
0 333 07445 9 (paper cover)

Printed in Great Britain by
UNWIN BROTHERS LIMITED
Old Woking, Surrey

What one fool can do, another can.
Ancient Simian proverb

PUBLISHERS' NOTE ON THE THIRD EDITION

ONLY once in its long and useful life, in 1919, has this book been enlarged and revised. But in twenty-four years much progress can be made, and the methods of 1919 are not likely to be the same as those of 1945. If, therefore, any book is to maintain its usefulness, it is essential that it should be overhauled occasionally so that it may be brought up-to-date where possible, to keep pace with the forward march of scientific development.

For the new edition the book has been reset, and the diagrams modernised. Mr. F. G. W. Brown has been good enough to revise the whole of the book, but he has taken great care not to interfere with the original plan. Thus teachers and students will still recognise their well-known guide to the intricacies of the calculus. While the changes made are not of a major kind, yet their significance may not be inconsiderable. There seems no reason now, even if one ever existed, for excluding from the scope of the text those intensely practical functions, known as the hyperbolic sine, cosine and tangent, whose applications to the methods of integration are so potent and manifold. These have, accordingly, been introduced and applied, with the result that some of the long cumbersome methods of integrating have been displaced, just as a ray of sunshine dispels an obstructing cloud.

The introduction, too, of the very practical integrals :

$$\int \epsilon^{pt} \sin kt \,.\, dt \quad \text{and} \quad \int \epsilon^{pt} \cos kt \,.\, dt$$

has eliminated some of the more ancient methods of " Finding Solutions " (Chapter XXI). By their application, shorter and more intelligible ones have grown up naturally instead.

In the treatment of substitutions, the whole text has been tidied up in order to render it methodically consistent. A few examples have also been added where space permitted, while the whole of the exercises and their answers have been carefully revised, checked and corrected. Duplicated problems have thus been removed and many hints provided in the answers adapted to the newer and more modern methods introduced.

It must, however, be emphatically stated that the plan of the original author remains unchanged ; even in its more modern form, the book still remains a monument to the skill and the courage of the late Professor Silvanus P. Thompson. All that the present reviser has attempted is to revitalize the usefulness of the work by adapting its distinctive utilitarian bias more closely in relation to present-day requirements.

CONTENTS

PROLOGUE

CONSIDERING how many fools can calculate, it is surprising that it should be thought either a difficult or a tedious task for any other fool to learn how to master the same tricks.

Some calculus-tricks are quite easy. Some are enormously difficult. The fools who write the text-books of advanced mathematics—and they are mostly clever fools—seldom take the trouble to show you how easy the easy calculations are. On the contrary, they seem to desire to impress you with their tremendous cleverness by going about it in the most difficult way.

Being myself a remarkably stupid fellow, I have had to unteach myself the difficulties, and now beg to present to my fellow fools the parts that are not hard. Master these thoroughly, and the rest will follow. What one fool can do, another can.

COMMON GREEK LETTERS USED AS SYMBOLS

Capital	Small	English Name	Capital	Small	English Name
A	α	Alpha	Λ	λ	Lambda
B	β	Beta	M	μ	Mu
Γ	γ	Gamma	Ξ	ξ	Xi
Δ	δ	Delta	Π	π	Pi
E	ϵ	Epsilon	P	ρ	Rho
H	η	Ēta	Σ	σ	Sigma
Θ	θ	Thēta	Φ	ϕ	Phi
K	κ	Kappa	Ω	ω	Omega

CHAPTER I

TO DELIVER YOU FROM THE PRELIMINARY TERRORS

THE preliminary terror, which chokes off most fifth-form boys from even attempting to learn how to calculate, can be abolished once for all by simply stating what is the meaning —in common-sense terms—of the two principal symbols that are used in calculating.

These dreadful symbols are :

(1) d which merely means " a little bit of ".

Thus dx means a little bit of x ; or du means a little bit of u. Ordinary mathematicians think it more polite to say " an element of ", instead of " a little bit of ". Just as you please. But you will find that these little bits (or elements) may be considered to be indefinitely small.

(2) $\int$ which is merely a long S, and may be called (if you like) " the sum of ".

Thus $\int dx$ means the sum of all the little bits of x ; or $\int dt$ means the sum of all the little bits of t. Ordinary mathematicians call this symbol " the integral of ". Now any fool can see that if x is considered as made up of a lot of little bits, each of which is called dx, if you add them all up together you get the sum of all the dx's (which is the same thing as the whole of x). The word " integral " simply means " the whole ". If you think of the duration of time for one hour, you may (if you like) think of it as cut up into 3600 little bits called seconds. The whole of the 3600 little bits added up together make one hour.

1

When you see an expression that begins with this terrifying symbol, you will henceforth know that it is put there merely to give you instructions that you are now to perform the operation (if you can) of totalling up all the little bits that are indicated by the symbols that follow.

That's all.

CHAPTER II

ON DIFFERENT DEGREES OF SMALLNESS

WE shall find that in our processes of calculation we have to deal with small quantities of various degrees of smallness.

We shall have also to learn under what circumstances we may consider small quantities to be so minute that we may omit them from consideration. Everything depends upon relative minuteness.

Before we fix any rules let us think of some familiar cases. There are 60 minutes in the hour, 24 hours in the day, 7 days in the week. There are therefore 1440 minutes in the day and 10,080 minutes in the week.

Obviously 1 minute is a very small quantity of time compared with a whole week. Indeed, our forefathers considered it small as compared with an hour, and called it " one minute ", meaning a minute fraction—namely one sixtieth—of an hour. When they came to require still smaller subdivisions of time, they divided each minute into 60 still smaller parts, which, in Queen Elizabeth's days, they called " second minutes " (*i.e.* small quantities of the second order of minuteness). Nowadays we call these small quantities of the second order of smallness " seconds ". But few people know *why* they are so called.

Now if one minute is so small as compared with a whole day, how much smaller by comparison is one second !

Again, think of a farthing as compared with a sovereign : it is worth only a little more than $\frac{1}{1000}$ part. A farthing more or less is of precious little importance compared with a sovereign : it may certainly be regarded as a *small* quantity. But compare a farthing with £1000 : relatively to this

3

greater sum, the farthing is of no more importance than
$\frac{1}{1000}$ of a farthing would be to a sovereign. Even a golden
sovereign is relatively a negligible quantity in the wealth of a
millionaire.

Now if we fix upon any numerical fraction as constituting
the proportion which for any purpose we call relatively small,
we can easily state other fractions of a higher degree of smallness.   Thus if, for the purpose of time, $\frac{1}{60}$ be called a *small*
fraction, then $\frac{1}{60}$ of $\frac{1}{60}$ (being a *small* fraction of a *small*
fraction) may be regarded as a *small quantity of the second
order* of smallness.*

Or, if for any purpose we were to take 1 per cent.
(*i.e.* $\frac{1}{100}$) as a *small* fraction, then 1 per cent. of 1 per cent.
(*i.e.* $\frac{1}{10,000}$) would be a small fraction of the second order
of smallness ; and $\frac{1}{1,000,000}$ would be a small fraction of the
third order of smallness, being 1 per cent. of 1 per cent. of
1 per cent.

Lastly, suppose that for some very precise purpose we
should regard $\frac{1}{1,000,000}$ as " small ".   Thus, if a first-rate
chronometer is not to lose or gain more than half a minute in
a year, it must keep time with an accuracy of 1 part in
1,051,200.   Now if, for such a purpose, we regard $\frac{1}{1,000,000}$ (or
one millionth) as a small quantity, then $\frac{1}{1,000,000}$ of $\frac{1}{1,000,000}$,
that is, $\frac{1}{1,000,000,000,000}$ (or one billionth) will be a small
quantity of the second order of smallness, and may be utterly
disregarded, by comparison.

Then we see that the smaller a small quantity itself is, the
more negligible does the corresponding small quantity of the
second order become.   Hence we know that *in all cases we are
justified in neglecting the small quantities of the second—or third*

* The mathematicians talk about the second order of " magnitude "
(*i.e.* greatness) when they really mean second order of *smallness*. This
is very confusing to beginners.

(or higher)—*orders*, if only we take the small quantity of the first order small enough in itself.

But it must be remembered that small quantities, if they occur in our expressions as factors multiplied by some other factor, may become important if the other factor is itself large. Even a farthing becomes important if only it is multiplied by a few hundred.

Now in the calculus we write dx for a little bit of x. These things such as dx, and du, and dy, are called " differentials ", the differential of x, or of u, or of y, as the case may be. [You *read* them as *dee-eks*, or *dee-you*, or *dee-wy*.] If dx be a small bit of x, and relatively small of itself, it does not follow that such quantities as $x \cdot dx$, or x^2dx, or a^xdx are negligible. But $dx \times dx$ would be negligible, being a small quantity of the second order.

A very simple example will serve as illustration.

Let us think of x as a quantity that can grow by a small amount so as to become $x + dx$, where dx is the small increment added by growth. The square of this is $x^2 + 2x \cdot dx + (dx)^2$. The second term is not negligible because it is a first-order quantity ; while the third term is of the second order of small-ness, being a bit of a bit of x. Thus if we took dx to mean numerically, say, $\frac{1}{60}$ of x, then the second term would be $\frac{2}{60}$ of x^2, whereas the third term would be $\frac{1}{3600}$ of x^2. This last term is clearly less important than the second. But if we go further and take dx to mean only $\frac{1}{1000}$ of x, then the second term will be $\frac{2}{1000}$ of x^2, while the third term will be only $\frac{1}{1,000,000}$ of x^2.

Geometrically this may be depicted as follows : Draw a square (Fig. 1) the side of which we will take to represent x. Now suppose the square to grow by having a bit dx added to its size each way. The enlarged square is made up of the original square x^2, the two rectangles at the top and on the right, each of which is of area $x \cdot dx$ (or together $2x \cdot dx$), and

Fig. 1.

the little square at the top right-hand corner which is $(dx)^2$.
In Fig. 2 we have taken dx as quite a big fraction of x—about
$\frac{1}{5}$. But suppose we had taken it only $\frac{1}{100}$—about the thickness of an inked line drawn with a fine pen. Then the little
corner square will have an area of only $\frac{1}{10,000}$ of x^2, and be
practically invisible. Clearly $(dx)^2$ is negligible if only we
consider the increment dx to be itself small enough.

Fig. 2.

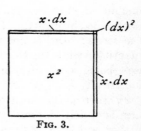

Fig. 3.

Let us consider a simile.

Suppose a millionaire were to say to his secretary : next
week I will give you a small fraction of any money that comes
in to me. Suppose that the secretary were to say to his boy :
I will give you a small fraction of what I get. Suppose the
fraction in each case to be $\frac{1}{100}$ part. Now if Mr. Millionaire
received during the next week £1000, the secretary would
receive £10 and the boy 2 shillings. Ten pounds would be a

small quantity compared with £1000 ; but two shillings is a small small quantity indeed, of a very secondary order. But what would be the disproportion if the fraction, instead of being $\frac{1}{100}$, had been settled at $\frac{1}{1000}$ part? Then, while Mr. Millionaire got his £1000, Mr. Secretary would get only £1, and the boy less than one farthing !

The witty Dean Swift * once wrote :

> " So, Nat'ralists observe, a Flea
> " Hath smaller Fleas that on him prey.
> " And these have smaller Fleas to bite 'em,
> " And so proceed *ad infinitum*."

An ox might worry about a flea of ordinary size—a small creature of the first order of smallness. But he would probably not trouble himself about a flea's flea ; being of the second order of smallness, it would be negligible. Even a gross of fleas' fleas would not be of much account to the ox.

* *On Poetry : a Rhapsody* (p. 20), printed 1733—usually misquoted.

CHAPTER III

ON RELATIVE GROWINGS

ALL through the calculus we are dealing with quantities that are growing, and with rates of growth. We classify all quantities into two classes : *constants* and *variables*. Those which we regard as of fixed value, and call *constants*, we generally denote algebraically by letters from the beginning of the alphabet, such as a, b, or c ; while those which we consider as capable of growing, or (as mathematicians say) of " varying ", we denote by letters from the end of the alphabet, such as x, y, z, u, v, w, or sometimes t.

Moreover, we are usually dealing with more than one variable at once, and thinking of the way in which one variable depends on the other : for instance, we think of the way in which the height reached by a projectile depends on the time of attaining that height. Or, we are asked to consider a rectangle of given area, and to enquire how any increase in the length of it will compel a corresponding decrease in the breadth of it. Or, we think of the way in which any variation in the slope of a ladder will cause the height that it reaches, to vary.

Suppose we have got two such variables that depend one on the other. An alteration in one will bring about an alteration in the other, *because* of this dependence. Let us call one of the variables x, and the other that depends on it y.

Suppose we make x to vary, that is to say, we either alter it or imagine it to be altered, by adding to it a bit which we call dx. We are thus causing x to become $x + dx$. Then, because x has been altered, y will have altered also, and will have become $y + dy$. Here the bit dy may be in some cases positive, in others negative ; and it won't (except very rarely) be the same size as dx.

8

Take two examples.

(1) Let x and y be respectively the base and the height of a right-angled triangle (Fig. 4), of which the slope of the other side is fixed at 30°. If we suppose this triangle to expand and yet keep its angles the same as at first, then,

Fig. 4.

when the base grows so as to become $x + dx$, the height becomes $y + dy$. Here, increasing x results in an increase of y. The little triangle, the height of which is dy, and the base of which is dx, is similar to the original triangle ; and it is obvious that the value of the ratio $\dfrac{dy}{dx}$ is the same as that of the ratio $\dfrac{y}{x}$. As the angle is 30° it will be seen that here

$$\frac{dy}{dx} = \frac{1}{1 \cdot 73}.$$

(2) Let x represent, in Fig. 5, the horizontal distance, from a wall, of the bottom end of a ladder, AB, of fixed length ; and let y be the height it reaches up the wall. Now y clearly

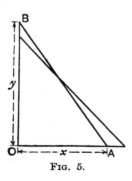

Fig. 5.

depends on x. It is easy to see that, if we pull the bottom end A ⌢ bit further from the wall, the top end B will come down a little lower. Let us state this in scientific language. If we increase x to $x + dx$, then y will become $y - dy$; that is, when x receives a positive increment, the increment which results to y is negative.

Yes, but how much? Suppose the ladder was so long that when the bottom end A was 19 inches from the wall the top end B reached just 15 feet from the ground. Now, if you were to pull the bottom end out 1 inch more, how much would the top end come down? Put it all into inches: $x = 19$ inches, $y = 180$ inches. Now the increment of x which we call dx, is 1 inch: or $x + dx = 20$ inches.

How much will y be diminished? The new height will be $y - dy$. If we work out the height by Euclid I. 47, then we shall be able to find how much dy will be. The length of the ladder is

$$\sqrt{(180)^2 + (19)^2} = 181 \text{ inches.}$$

Clearly, then, the new height, which is $y - dy$, will be such that

$$(y - dy)^2 = (181)^2 - (20)^2 = 32761 - 400 = 32361,$$
$$y - dy = \sqrt{32361} = 179 \cdot 89 \text{ inches.}$$

Now y is 180, so that dy is $180 - 179 \cdot 89 = 0 \cdot 11$ inch.

So we see that making dx an increase of 1 inch has resulted in making dy a decrease of $0 \cdot 11$ inch.

And the ratio of dy to dx may be stated thus:

$$\frac{dy}{dx} = -\frac{0 \cdot 11}{1}.$$

It is also easy to see that (except in one particular position) dy will be of a different size from dx.

Now right through the differential calculus we are hunting, hunting, hunting for a curious thing, a mere ratio, namely, the proportion which dy bears to dx when both of them are indefinitely small.

It should be noted here that we can only find this ratio $\frac{dy}{dx}$ when y and x are related to each other in some way, so that whenever x varies y does vary also. For instance, in the first example just taken, if the base x of the triangle be made longer, the height y of the triangle becomes greater also, and in the second example, if the distance x of the foot of the ladder from the wall be made to increase, the height y reached by the ladder decreases in a corresponding manner, slowly at first, but more and more rapidly as x becomes greater. In these cases the relation between x and y is perfectly definite, it can be expressed mathematically, being $\frac{y}{x} = \tan 30°$ and $x^2 + y^2 = l^2$ (where l is the length of the ladder) respectively, and $\frac{dy}{dx}$ has the meaning we found in each case.

If, while x is, as before, the distance of the foot of the ladder from the wall, y is, instead of the height reached, the horizontal length of the wall, or the number of bricks in it, or the number of years since it was built, any change in x would naturally cause no change whatever in y ; in this case $\frac{dy}{dx}$ has no meaning whatever, and it is not possible to find an expression for it. Whenever we use differentials dx, dy, dz, etc., the existence of some kind of relation between x, y, z, etc., is implied, and this relation is called a " function " in x, y, z, etc. ; the two expressions given above, for instance, namely, $\frac{y}{x} = \tan 30°$ and $x^2 + y^2 = l^2$, are functions of x and y. Such expressions contain implicitly (that is, contain without distinctly showing it) the means of expressing either x in terms of y or y in terms of x, and for this reason they are called *implicit functions in x and y* ; they can be respectively put into the forms

$$y = x \tan 30° \quad \text{or} \quad x = \frac{y}{\tan 30°}$$

and
$$y = \sqrt{l^2 - x^2} \quad \text{or} \quad x = \sqrt{l^2 - y^2}.$$

These last expressions state explicitly (that is, distinctly) the value of x in terms of y, or of y in terms of x, and they are for this reason called *explicit functions* of x or y. For example

$x^2 + 3 = 2y - 7$ is an implicit function in x and y ; it may be written $y = \dfrac{x^2 + 10}{2}$ (explicit function of x) or $x = \sqrt{2y - 10}$ (explicit function of y). We see that an explicit function in x, y, z, etc., is simply something the value of which changes when x, y, z, etc., are changing, either one at the time or several together. Because of this, the value of the explicit function is called the *dependent variable*, as it depends on the value of the other variable quantities in the function ; these other variables are called the *independent variables* because their value is not determined from the value assumed by the function. For example, if $u = x^2 \sin \theta$, x and θ are the independent variables, and u is the dependent variable.

Sometimes the exact relation between several quantities x, y, z either is not known or it is not convenient to state it ; it is only known, or convenient to state, that there is some sort of relation between these variables, so that one cannot alter either x or y or z singly without affecting the other quantities ; the existence of a function in x, y, z is then indicated by the notation $F(x, y, z)$ (implicit function) or by $x = F(y, z)$, $y = F(x, z)$ or $z = F(x, y)$ (explicit function). Sometimes the letter f or ϕ is used instead of F, so that $y = F(x)$, $y = f(x)$ and $y = \phi(x)$ all mean the same thing, namely, that the value of y depends on the value of x in some way which is not stated.

We call the ratio $\dfrac{dy}{dx}$, " the *differential coefficient* of y with respect to x ". It is a solemn scientific name for this very simple thing. But we are not going to be frightened by solemn names, when the things themselves are so easy. Instead of being frightened we will simply pronounce a brief curse on the stupidity of giving long crack-jaw names ; and, having relieved our minds, will go on to the simple thing itself, namely the ratio $\dfrac{dy}{dx}$.

In ordinary algebra which you learned at school, you were always hunting after some unknown quantity which you called x or y; or sometimes there were two unknown quantities to be hunted for simultaneously. You have now to learn to go hunting in a new way; the fox being now neither x nor y. Instead of this you have to hunt for this curious cub called $\frac{dy}{dx}$. The process of finding the value of $\frac{dy}{dx}$ is called " differentiating ". But, remember, what is wanted is the value of this ratio when both dy and dx are themselves indefinitely small. The true value of the differential coefficient is that to which it approximates in the limiting case when each of them is considered as infinitesimally minute.

Let us now learn how to go in quest of $\frac{dy}{dx}$.

NOTE TO CHAPTER III

How to read Differentials

It will never do to fall into the schoolboy error of thinking that dx means d times x, for d is not a factor—it means " an element of " or " a bit of " whatever follows. One reads dx thus : " dee-eks ".

In case the reader has no one to guide him in such matters it may here be simply said that one reads differential coefficients in the following way. The differential coefficient

$\frac{dy}{dx}$ is read " *dee-wy by dee-eks* ", or " *dee-wy over dee-eks* ".

So also $\frac{du}{dt}$ is read " *dee-you by dee-tee* ".

Second differential coefficients will be met with later on. They are like this :

$\frac{d^2y}{dx^2}$; which is read " *dee-two-wy over dee-eks-squared* ", and it means that the operation of differentiating y with respect to x has been (or has to be) performed twice over.

Another way of indicating that a function has been differentiated is by putting an accent to the symbol of the function. Thus if $y = F(x)$, which means that y is some unspecified function of x (see p. 12), we may write $F'(x)$ instead of $\dfrac{d(F(x))}{dx}$. Similarly, $F''(x)$ will mean that the original function $F(x)$ has been differentiated twice over with respect to x.

CHAPTER IV

SIMPLEST CASES

Now let us see how, on first principles, we can differentiate some simple algebraical expression.

Case 1.

Let us begin with the simple expression $y = x^2$. Now remember that the fundamental notion about the calculus is the idea of *growing*. Mathematicians call it *varying*. Now as y and x^2 are equal to one another, it is clear that if x grows, x^2 will also grow. And if x^2 grows, then y will also grow. What we have got to find out is the proportion between the growing of y and the growing of x. In other words, our task is to find out the ratio between dy and dx, or, in brief, to find the value of $\frac{dy}{dx}$.

Let x, then, grow a little bit bigger and become $x + dx$; similarly, y will grow a bit bigger and will become $y + dy$. Then, clearly, it will still be true that the enlarged y will be equal to the square of the enlarged x. Writing this down, we have :
$$y + dy = (x + dx)^2.$$

Doing the squaring we get :
$$y + dy = x^2 + 2x \cdot dx + (dx)^2.$$

What does $(dx)^2$ mean? Remember that dx meant a bit— a little bit—of x. Then $(dx)^2$ will mean a little bit of a little bit of x; that is, as explained above (p. 3), it is a small quantity of the second order of smallness. It may therefore be discarded as quite inconsiderable in comparison with the other terms. Leaving it out, we then have :
$$y + dy = x^2 + 2x \cdot dx.$$

Now $y = x^2$; so let us subtract this from the equation and we have left

$$dy = 2x \,.\, dx.$$

Dividing across by dx, we find

$$\frac{dy}{dx} = 2x.$$

Now *this* * is what we set out to find. The ratio of the growing of y to the growing of x is, in the case before us, found to be $2x$.

Numerical example.

Suppose $x = 100$ and $\therefore \; y = 10,000$. Then let x grow till it becomes 101 (that is, let $dx = 1$). Then the enlarged y will be $101 \times 101 = 10,201$. But if we agree that we may ignore small quantities of the second order, 1 may be rejected as compared with 10,000 ; so we may round off the enlarged y to 10,200. y has grown from 10,000 to 10,200 ; the bit added on is dy, which is therefore 200.

$\frac{dy}{dx} = \frac{200}{1} = 200.$ According to the algebra-working of the previous paragraph, we find $\frac{dy}{dx} = 2x$. And so it is ; for $x = 100$ and $2x = 200$.

---

* *N.B.*—This ratio $\frac{dy}{dx}$ is the result of differentiating y with respect to x. Differentiating means finding the differential coefficient. Suppose we had some other function of x, as, for example, $u = 7x^2 + 3$. Then if we were told to differentiate this with respect to x, we should have to find $\frac{du}{dx}$, or, what is the same thing, $\frac{d(7x^2 + 3)}{dx}$. On the other hand, we may have a case in which time was the independent variable (see p. 12), such as this : $y = b + \frac{1}{2}at^2$. Then, if we were told to differentiate it, that means we must find its differential coefficient with respect to t. So that then our business would be to try to find $\frac{dy}{dt}$, that is, to find $\frac{d(b + \frac{1}{2}at^2)}{dt}$.

But, you will say, we neglected a whole unit.

Well, try again, making dx a still smaller bit.

Try $dx = \frac{1}{10}$. Then $x + dx = 100.1$, and

$$(x + dx)^2 = 100.1 \times 100.1 = 10{,}020.01.$$

Now the last figure 1 is only one-millionth part of the 10,000, and is utterly negligible ; so we may take 10,020 without the little decimal at the end. And this makes $dy = 20$; and $\frac{dy}{dx} = \frac{20}{0.1} = 200$, which is still the same as $2x$.

Case 2.

Try differentiating $y = x^3$ in the same way.

We let y grow to $y + dy$, while x grows to $x + dx$.

Then we have $\qquad y + dy = (x + dx)^3.$

Doing the cubing we obtain

$$y + dy = x^3 + 3x^2 \cdot dx + 3x(dx)^2 + (dx)^3.$$

Now we know that we may neglect small quantities of the second and third orders ; since, when dy and dx are both made indefinitely small, $(dx)^2$ and $(dx)^3$ will become indefinitely smaller by comparison. So, regarding them as negligible, we have left : $\qquad y + dy = x^3 + 3x^2 \cdot dx.$

But $y = x^3$; and, subtracting this, we have :

$$dy = 3x^2 \cdot dx,$$

and $\qquad\qquad \dfrac{dy}{dx} = 3x^2.$

Case 3.

Try differentiating $y = x^4$. Starting as before by letting both y and x grow a bit, we have :

$$y + dy = (x + dx)^4.$$

Working out the raising to the fourth power, we get

$$y + dy = x^4 + 4x^3 dx + 6x^2(dx)^2 + 4x(dx)^3 + (dx)^4.$$

Then, striking out the terms containing all the higher

powers of dx, as being negligible by comparison, we have
$$y + dy = x^4 + 4x^3dx.$$
Subtracting the original $y = x^4$, we have left

$$dy = 4x^3dx, \quad \text{and} \quad \frac{dy}{dx} = 4x^3.$$

Now all these cases are quite easy. Let us collect the results to see if we can infer any general rule. Put them in two columns, the values of y in one and the corresponding values found for $\frac{dy}{dx}$ in the other : thus

y	$\dfrac{dy}{dx}$
x^2	$2x$
x^3	$3x^2$
x^4	$4x^3$

Just look at these results : the operation of differentiating appears to have had the effect of diminishing the power of x by 1 (for example in the last case reducing x^4 to x^3), and at the same time multiplying by a number (the same number in fact which originally appeared as the power). Now, when you have once seen this, you might easily conjecture how the others will run. You would expect that differentiating x^5 would give $5x^4$, or differentiating x^6 would give $6x^5$. If you hesitate, try one of these, and see whether the conjecture comes right.

Try $y = x^5$.

Then $y + dy = (x + dx)^5 = x^5 + 5x^4dx + 10x^3(dx)^2 + 10x^2(dx)^3$
$$+ 5x(dx)^4 + (dx)^5.$$

Neglecting all the terms containing small quantities of the higher orders, we have left

$$y + dy = x^5 + 5x^4 dx.$$

and subtracting $y = x^5$ leaves us

$$dy = 5x^4 dx,$$

whence $\quad\quad\quad \dfrac{dy}{dx} = 5x^4$, exactly as we supposed.

Following out logically our observation, we should conclude that if we want to deal with any higher power—call it x^n—we could tackle it in the same way.

Let $\quad\quad\quad\quad\quad y = x^n,$

then we should expect to find that

$$\frac{dy}{dx} = nx^{n-1}.$$

For example, let $n = 8$, then $y = x^8$; and differentiating it would give $\dfrac{dy}{dx} = 8x^7$.

And, indeed, the rule that differentiating x^n gives as the result nx^{n-1} is true for all cases where n is a whole number and positive. [Expanding $(x + dx)^n$ by the binomial theorem will at once show this.] But the question whether it is true for cases where n has negative or fractional values requires further consideration.

Case of a negative index.

Let $y = x^{-2}$. Then proceed as before :

$$y + dy = (x + dx)^{-2}$$
$$= x^{-2}\left(1 + \frac{dx}{x}\right)^{-2}.$$

Expanding this by the binomial theorem (see p. 116), we get

$$= x^{-2}\left[1 - \frac{2dx}{x} + \frac{2(2+1)}{1 \times 2}\left(\frac{dx}{x}\right)^2 - \text{etc.}\right]$$

$$= x^{-2} - 2x^{-3} \cdot dx + 3x^{-4}(dx)^2 - 4x^{-5}(dx)^3 + \text{etc.}$$

So, neglecting the small quantities of higher orders of smallness, we have :

$$y + dy = x^{-2} - 2x^{-3} \cdot dx.$$

Subtracting the original $y = x^{-2}$, we find

$$dy = -2x^{-3}dx,$$

$$\frac{dy}{dx} = -2x^{-3}.$$

And this is still in accordance with the rule inferred above.

Case of a fractional index.

Let $y = x^{\frac{1}{2}}$. Then, as before,

$$y + dy = (x + dx)^{\frac{1}{2}} = x^{\frac{1}{2}}\left(1 + \frac{dx}{x}\right)^{\frac{1}{2}} = \sqrt{x}\left(1 + \frac{dx}{x}\right)^{\frac{1}{2}}$$

$$= \sqrt{x} + \frac{1}{2}\frac{dx}{\sqrt{x}} - \frac{1}{8}\frac{(dx)^2}{x\sqrt{x}} + \text{terms with higher powers of } dx.$$

Subtracting the original $y = x^{\frac{1}{2}}$, and neglecting higher powers we have left :

$$dy = \frac{1}{2}\frac{dx}{\sqrt{x}} = \frac{1}{2}x^{-\frac{1}{2}} \cdot dx,$$

and $\quad \dfrac{dy}{dx} = \dfrac{1}{2}x^{-\frac{1}{2}}$. This agrees with the general rule.

Summary. Let us see how far we have got. We have arrived at the following rule : To differentiate x^n, multiply it by the index and reduce the index by one, so giving us nx^{n-1} as the result.

EXERCISES I

(See page 240 for Answers)

Differentiate the following :

(1) $y = x^{13}$.   (2) $y = x^{-\frac{3}{2}}$.

(3) $y = x^{2a}$.   (4) $u = t^{2 \cdot 4}$.

(5) $z = \sqrt[3]{u}$.   (6) $y = \sqrt[3]{x^{-5}}$.

(7) $u = \sqrt[5]{\dfrac{1}{x^8}}$.   (8) $y = 2x^a$.

(9) $y = \sqrt[q]{x^3}$.   (10) $y = \sqrt[n]{\dfrac{1}{x^m}}$.

You have now learned how to differentiate powers of x.   How easy it is !

CHAPTER V

NEXT STAGE. WHAT TO DO WITH CONSTANTS

In our equations we have regarded x as growing, and as a result of x being made to grow y also changed its value and grew. We usually think of x as a quantity that we can vary ; and, regarding the variation of x as a sort of *cause*, we consider the resulting variation of y as an *effect*. In other words, we regard the value of y as depending on that of x. Both x and y are variables, but x is the one that we operate upon, and y is the " dependent variable ". In all the preceding chapter we have been trying to find out rules for the proportion which the dependent variation in y bears to the variation independently made in x.

Our next step is to find out what effect on the process of differentiating is caused by the presence of *constants*, that is, of numbers which don't change when x or y changes its value.

Added Constants.

Let us begin with some simple case of an added constant, thus :

Let $$y = x^3 + 5.$$

Just as before, let us suppose x to grow to $x + dx$ and y to grow to $y + dy$.

Then : $$y + dy = (x + dx)^3 + 5$$
$$= x^3 + 3x^2 dx + 3x(dx)^2 + (dx)^3 + 5.$$

Neglecting the small quantities of higher orders, this becomes

$$y + dy = x^3 + 3x^2 \cdot dx + 5.$$

Subtract the original $y = x^3 + 5$, and we have left :

$$dy = 3x^2 dx.$$

$$\frac{dy}{dx} = 3x^2.$$

So the 5 has quite disappeared. It added nothing to the growth of x, and does not enter into the differential coefficient. If we had put 7, or 700, or any other number, instead of 5, it would have disappeared. So if we take the letter a, or b, or c to represent any constant, it will simply disappear when we differentiate.

If the additional constant had been of negative value, such as -5 or $-b$, it would equally have disappeared.

Multiplied Constants.

Take as a simple experiment this case :

Let $y = 7x^2$.

Then on proceeding as before we get :

$$y + dy = 7(x + dx)^2$$
$$= 7\{x^2 + 2x \cdot dx + (dx)^2\}$$
$$= 7x^2 + 14x \cdot dx + 7(dx)^2.$$

Then, subtracting the original $y = 7x^2$, and neglecting the last term, we have

$$dy = 14x \cdot dx.$$

$$\frac{dy}{dx} = 14x.$$

Let us illustrate this example by working out the graphs of the equations $y = 7x^2$ and $\frac{dy}{dx} = 14x$, by assigning to x a set of successive values, 0, 1, 2, 3, etc., and finding the corresponding values of y and of $\frac{dy}{dx}$.

These values we tabulate as follows :

x	0	1	2	3	4	5	− 1	− 2	− 3
y	0	7	28	63	112	175	7	28	63
$\dfrac{dy}{dx}$	0	14	28	42	56	70	− 14	− 28	− 42

Now plot these values to some convenient scale, and we obtain the two curves, Figs. 6 and 6a.

FIG. 6.—Graph of $y = 7x^2$.   FIG. 6a.—Graph of $\dfrac{dy}{dx} = 14x$.

Carefully compare the two figures, and verify by inspection that the height of the ordinate of the derived curve, Fig. 6a, is proportional to the *slope* of the original curve,* Fig. 6, at the corresponding value of x. To the left of the origin, where the original curve slopes negatively (that is, downward from left to right) the corresponding ordinates of the derived curve are negative.

Now, if we look back at pp. 15–16, we shall see that simply differentiating x^2 gives us $2x$. So that the differential coeffi-

---

* See p. 66 about *slopes* of curves.

cient of $7x^2$ is just 7 times as big as that of x^2. If we had taken $8x^2$, the differential coefficient would have come out eight times as great as that of x^2. If we put $y = ax^2$, we shall get

$$\frac{dy}{dx} = a \times 2x.$$

If we had begun with $y = ax^n$, we should have had

$$\frac{dy}{dx} = a \times nx^{n-1}.$$

So that any mere multiplication by a constant reappears as a mere multiplication when the thing is differentiated. And, what is true about multiplication is equally true about *division* : for if, in the example above, we had taken as the constant $\frac{1}{7}$ instead of 7, we should have had the same $\frac{1}{7}$ come out in the result after differentiation.

Some Further Examples.

The following further examples, fully worked out, will enable you to master completely the process of differentiation as applied to ordinary algebraical expressions, and enable you to work out by yourself the examples given at the end of this chapter.

(1) Differentiate $y = \dfrac{x^5}{7} - \dfrac{3}{5}$.

$-\dfrac{3}{5}$ is an added constant and vanishes (see p. 22).

We may then write at once

$$\frac{dy}{dx} = \frac{1}{7} \times 5 \times x^{5-1},$$

or
$$\frac{dy}{dx} = \frac{5}{7} x^4.$$

(2) Differentiate $y = a\sqrt{x} - \frac{1}{2}\sqrt{a}$.

The term $-\frac{1}{2}\sqrt{a}$ vanishes, being an added constant; and as $a\sqrt{x}$, in the index form, is written $ax^{\frac{1}{2}}$, we have

$$\frac{dy}{dx} = a \times \frac{1}{2} \times x^{\frac{1}{2}-1} = \frac{a}{2} \times x^{-\frac{1}{2}},$$

or

$$\frac{dy}{dx} = \frac{a}{2\sqrt{x}}.$$

(3) If $\quad ay + bx = by - ax + (x+y)\sqrt{a^2 - b^2}$,

find the differential coefficient of y with respect to x.

As a rule an expression of this kind will need a little more knowledge than we have acquired so far; it is, however, always worth while to try whether the expression can be put into the form $y =$ some expression involving x only.

The expression may be written

$$(a-b)y + (a+b)x = (x+y)\sqrt{a^2 - b^2}.$$

Write k^2 for $\frac{a+b}{a-b}$, then

$$a^2 - b^2 = (a+b)(a-b) = k^2(a-b)^2,$$

$$\therefore \quad \sqrt{a^2 - b^2} = k(a-b).$$

Hence $\quad (a-b)y + (a+b)x = (x+y)k(a-b)$.

Divide out by $(a-b)$, assuming a is not equal to b, then

$$y + k^2 x = k(x+y),$$

or $\quad\quad y(1-k) = kx(1-k),$

that is, $\quad\quad\quad y = kx.$

Hence $\quad\quad \frac{dy}{dx} = k = \sqrt{\frac{a+b}{a-b}}.$

(4) The volume of a cylinder of radius r and height h is given by the formula $V = \pi r^2 h$. Find the rate of variation of volume with the radius when $r = 5 \cdot 5$ in. and $h = 20$ in. If

$r = h$, find the dimensions of the cylinder so that a change of 1 in. in radius causes a change of 400 cub. in. in the volume.

The rate of variation of V with regard to r is

$$\frac{dV}{dr} = 2\pi r h.$$

If $r = 5 \cdot 5$ in. and $h = 20$ in. this becomes 690·8. It means that a change of radius of 1 inch will cause a change of volume of 690·8 cub. in. This can be easily verified, for the volumes with $r = 5$ and $r = 6$ are 1570 cub. in. and 2260·8 cub. in. respectively, and $2260 \cdot 8 - 1570 = 690 \cdot 8$.

Also, if $h = r$, and h remains constant,

$$\frac{dV}{dr} = 2\pi r^2 = 400 \quad \text{and} \quad r = h = \sqrt{\frac{400}{2\pi}} = 7 \cdot 98 \text{ in.}$$

If, however, $h = r$ and varies with r, then

$$\frac{dV}{dr} = 3\pi r^2 = 400 \quad \text{and} \quad r = h = \sqrt{\frac{400}{3\pi}} = 6 \cdot 51 \text{ in.}$$

(5) The reading θ of a Féry's Radiation pyrometer is related to the centigrade temperature t of the observed body by the relation $\theta/\theta_1 = (t/t_1)^4$, where θ_1 is the reading corresponding to a known temperature t_1 of the observed body.

Compare the sensitiveness of the pyrometer at temperatures 800° C., 1000° C., 1200° C., given that it read 25 when the temperature was 1000° C.

The sensitiveness is the rate of variation of the reading with the temperature, that is, $\dfrac{d\theta}{dt}$. The formula may be written

$$\theta = \frac{\theta_1}{t_1^4} t^4 = \frac{25t^4}{1000^4},$$

and we have

$$\frac{d\theta}{dt} = \frac{100t^3}{1000^4} = \frac{t^3}{10,000,000,000}.$$

When $t = 800$, 1000 and 1200, we get $\dfrac{d\theta}{dt} = 0 \cdot 0512$, 0·1 and 0·1728 respectively.

The sensitiveness is approximately doubled from 800° to 1000°, and becomes three-quarters as great again up to 1200°.

EXERCISES II

(*See page* 240 *for Answers*)

Differentiate the following :

(1) $y = ax^3 + 6$.

(2) $y = 13x^{\frac{3}{2}} - c$.

(3) $y = 12x^{\frac{1}{2}} + c^{\frac{1}{2}}$.

(4) $y = c^{\frac{1}{2}}x^{\frac{1}{2}}$.

(5) $u = \dfrac{az^n - 1}{c}$.

(6) $y = 1\cdot18t^2 + 22\cdot4$.

Make up some other examples for yourself, and try your hand at differentiating them.

(7) If l_t and l_0 be the lengths of a rod of iron at the temperatures $t°$ C. and $0°$ C. respectively, then $l_t = l_0(1 + 0\cdot000012t)$. Find the change of length of the rod per degree centigrade.

(8) It has been found that if c be the candle power of an incandescent electric lamp, and V be the voltage, $c = aV^b$, where a and b are constants.

Find the rate of change of the candle power with the voltage, and calculate the change of candle power per volt at 80, 100 and 120 volts in the case of a lamp for which $a = 0\cdot5 \times 10^{-10}$ and $b = 6$.

(9) The frequency n of vibration of a string of diameter D, length L and specific gravity σ, stretched with a force T, is given by

$$n = \frac{1}{DL} \sqrt{\frac{gT}{\pi\sigma}}.$$

Find the rate of change of the frequency when D, L, σ and T are varied singly.

(10) The greatest external pressure P which a tube can support without collapsing is given by

$$P = \left(\frac{2E}{1 - \sigma^2}\right)\frac{t^3}{D^3},$$

where E and σ are constants, t is the thickness of the tube and D is its diameter. (This formula assumes that $4t$ is small compared to D.)

Compare the rate at which P varies for a small change of thickness and for a small change of diameter taking place separately.

(11) Find, from first principles, the rate at which the following vary with respect to a change in radius :

    (a) the circumference of a circle of radius r ;
    (b) the area of a circle of radius r ;
    (c) the lateral area of a cone of slant dimension l ;
    (d) the volume of a cone of radius r and height h ;
    (e) the area of a sphere of radius r ;
    (f) the volume of a sphere of radius r.

(12) The length L of an iron rod at the temperature T being given by $L = l_t[1 + 0{\cdot}000012(T - t)]$, where l_t is the length at the temperature t, find the rate of variation of the diameter D of an iron tyre suitable for being shrunk on a wheel, when the temperature T varies.

CHAPTER VI

SUMS, DIFFERENCES, PRODUCTS, AND QUOTIENTS

WE have learned how to differentiate simple algebraical functions such as $x^2 + c$ or ax^4, and we have now to consider how to tackle the *sum* of two or more functions.

For instance, let

$$y = (x^2 + c) + (ax^4 + b) ;$$

what will its $\frac{dy}{dx}$ be? How are we to go to work on this new job?

The answer to this question is quite simple : just differentiate them, one after the other, thus :

$$\frac{dy}{dx} = 2x + 4ax^3.$$

If you have any doubt whether this is right, try a more general case, working it by first principles. And this is the way.

Let $y = u + v$, where u is any function of x, and v any other function of x. Then, letting x increase to $x + dx$, y will increase to $y + dy$; and u will increase to $u + du$; and v to $v + dv$.

And we shall have :

$$y + dy = u + du + v + dv.$$

Subtracting the original $y = u + v$, we get

$$dy = du + dv,$$

30

and dividing through by dx, we get :

$$\frac{dy}{dx} = \frac{du}{dx} + \frac{dv}{dx}.$$

This justifies the procedure. You differentiate each function separately and add the results. So if now we take the example of the preceding paragraph, and put in the values of the two functions, we shall have, using the notation shown (p. 13),

$$\frac{dy}{dx} = \frac{d(x^2 + c)}{dx} + \frac{d(ax^4 + b)}{dx}$$
$$= 2x \qquad + 4ax^3,$$

exactly as before.

If there were three functions of x, which we may call u, v and w, so that

$$y = u + v + w ;$$

then

$$\frac{dy}{dx} = \frac{du}{dx} + \frac{dv}{dx} + \frac{dw}{dx}.$$

As for the rule about *subtraction*, it follows at once ; for if the function v had itself had a negative sign, its differential coefficient would also be negative ; so that by differentiating

$$y = u - v,$$

we should get

$$\frac{dy}{dx} = \frac{du}{dx} - \frac{dv}{dx}.$$

But when we come to do with *Products*, the thing is not quite so simple.

Suppose we were asked to differentiate the expression

$$y = (x^2 + c) \times (ax^4 + b),$$

what are we to do? The result will certainly *not* be $2x \times 4ax^3$; for it is easy to see that neither $c \times ax^4$, nor $x^2 \times b$, would have been taken into that product.

Now there are two ways in which we may go to work.

First way. Do the multiplying first, and, having worked it out, then differentiate.

Accordingly, we multiply together $x^2 + c$ and $ax^4 + b$.

This gives $ax^6 + acx^4 + bx^2 + bc$.

Now differentiate, and we get :

$$\frac{dy}{dx} = 6ax^5 + 4acx^3 + 2bx.$$

Second way. Go back to first principles, and consider the equation

$$y = u \times v \ ;$$

where u is one function of x, and v is any other function of x. Then, if x grows to be $x + dx$; and y to $y + dy$; and u becomes $u + du$; and v becomes $v + dv$, we shall have:

$$y + dy = (u + du) \times (v + dv)$$

$$= u \cdot v + u \cdot dv + v \cdot du + du \cdot dv.$$

Now $du \cdot dv$ is a small quantity of the second order of smallness, and therefore in the limit may be discarded, leaving

$$y + dy = u \cdot v + u \cdot dv + v \cdot du.$$

Then, subtracting the original $y = u \cdot v$, we have left

$$dy = u \cdot dv + v \cdot du \ ;$$

and, dividing through by dx, we get the result :

$$\frac{dy}{dx} = u \frac{dv}{dx} + v \frac{du}{dx}.$$

This shows that our instructions will be as follows : *To differentiate the product of two functions, multiply each function by the differential coefficient of the other, and add together the two products so obtained.*

You should note that this process amounts to the following : Treat u as constant while you differentiate v ; then treat v as constant while you differentiate u ; and the whole differential coefficient $\dfrac{dy}{dx}$ will be the sum of the results of these two treatments.

Now, having found this rule, apply it to the concrete example which was considered above.

We want to differentiate the product

$$(x^2 + c) \times (ax^4 + b).$$

Call $\qquad (x^2 + c) = u$;   and $(ax^4 + b) = v.$

Then, by the general rule just established, we may write :

$$\frac{dy}{dx} = (x^2 + c)\,\frac{d(ax^4 + b)}{dx} + (ax^4 + b)\,\frac{d(x^2 + c)}{dx}$$

$$= (x^2 + c)\,4ax^3 \qquad + (ax^4 + b)\,2x$$

$$= 4ax^5 + 4acx^3 \qquad + 2ax^5 + 2bx,$$

$$\frac{dy}{dx} = 6ax^5 + 4acx^3 \qquad + 2bx,$$

exactly as before.

Lastly, we have to differentiate *quotients*.

Think of this example, $y = \dfrac{bx^5 + c}{x^2 + a}$.   In such a case it is no use to try to work out the division beforehand, because $x^2 + a$ will not divide into $bx^5 + c$, neither have they any common factor. So there is nothing for it but to go back to first principles, and find a rule.

So we will put $\qquad\qquad y = \dfrac{u}{v}$,

where u and v are two different functions of the independent variable x.   Then, when x becomes $x + dx$, y will become $y + dy$; and u will become $u + du$; and v will become $v + dv$. So then

$$y + dy = \frac{u + du}{v + dv}\,.$$

Now perform the algebraic division, thus :

$$v+dv \,\Big)\, \dfrac{u+du}{u+\dfrac{u\cdot dv}{v}} \,\Bigg|\, \dfrac{u}{v}+\dfrac{du}{v}-\dfrac{u\cdot dv}{v^2}$$

$$du-\dfrac{u\cdot dv}{v}$$

$$du+\dfrac{du\cdot dv}{v}$$

$$-\dfrac{u\cdot dv}{v}-\dfrac{du\cdot dv}{v}$$

$$-\dfrac{u\cdot dv}{v}-\dfrac{u\cdot dv\cdot dv}{v^2}$$

$$-\dfrac{du\cdot dv}{v}+\dfrac{u\cdot dv\cdot dv}{v^2}\,.$$

As both these remainders are small quantities of the second order, they may be neglected, and the division may stop here, since any further remainders would be of still smaller magnitudes.

So we have got :

$$y+dy = \frac{u}{v}+\frac{du}{v}-\frac{u\cdot dv}{v^2}\,;$$

which may be written

$$= \frac{u}{v}+\frac{v\cdot du-u\cdot dv}{v^2}\,.$$

Now subtract the original $y=\dfrac{u}{v}$, and we have left :

$$dy = \frac{v\cdot du-u\cdot dv}{v^2}\,;$$

whence

$$\frac{dy}{dx} = \frac{v\,\dfrac{du}{dx}-u\,\dfrac{dv}{dx}}{v^2}\,.$$

This gives us our instructions as to *how to differentiate a quotient* of two functions. *Multiply the divisor function by the differential coefficient of the dividend function ; then multiply the dividend function by the differential coefficient of the divisor function ; and subtract the latter product from the former. Lastly, divide the difference by the square of the divisor function.*

Going back to our example $y = \dfrac{bx^5 + c}{x^2 + a}$,

write $\qquad bx^5 + c = u ; \quad$ and $\quad x^2 + a = v.$

Then $\quad \dfrac{dy}{dx} = \dfrac{(x^2 + a)\dfrac{d(bx^5 + c)}{dx} - (bx^5 + c)\dfrac{d(x^2 + a)}{dx}}{(x^2 + a)^2}$

$\qquad\quad = \dfrac{(x^2 + a)(5bx^4) - (bx^5 + c)(2x)}{(x^2 + a)^2},$

$\dfrac{dy}{dx} = \dfrac{3bx^6 + 5abx^4 - 2cx}{(x^2 + a)^2}.$

The working out of quotients is often tedious, but there is nothing difficult about it.

Some further examples fully worked out are given hereafter.

(1) Differentiate $\quad y = \dfrac{a}{b^2}x^3 - \dfrac{a^2}{b}x + \dfrac{a^2}{b^2}.$

Being a constant, $\dfrac{a^2}{b^2}$ vanishes, and we have

$$\frac{dy}{dx} = \frac{a}{b^2} \times 3 \times x^{3-1} - \frac{a^2}{b} \times 1 \times x^{1-1}.$$

But $x^{1-1} = x^0 = 1$; so we get :

$$\frac{dy}{dx} = \frac{3a}{b^2}x^2 - \frac{a^2}{b}.$$

(2) Differentiate $\quad y = 2a\sqrt{bx^3} - \dfrac{3b\sqrt[3]{a}}{x} - 2\sqrt{ab.}$

Putting x in the index form, we get

$$y = 2a\sqrt{b}\, x^{\frac{3}{2}} - 3b\sqrt[3]{a}\, x^{-1} - 2\sqrt{ab}.$$

Now $\dfrac{dy}{dx} = 2a\sqrt{b} \times \frac{3}{2} \times x^{\frac{3}{2}-1} - 3b\sqrt[3]{a} \times (-1) \times x^{-1-1}$;

or, $\dfrac{dy}{dx} = 3a\sqrt{bx} + \dfrac{3b\sqrt[3]{a}}{x^2}$.

(3) Differentiate $z = 1{\cdot}8\sqrt[3]{\dfrac{1}{\theta^2}} - \dfrac{4{\cdot}4}{\sqrt[5]{\theta}} - 27°$.

This may be written : $z = 1{\cdot}8\theta^{-\frac{2}{3}} - 4{\cdot}4\theta^{-\frac{1}{5}} - 27°$.
The 27° vanishes, and we have

$$\frac{dz}{d\theta} = 1{\cdot}8 \times \left(-\tfrac{2}{3}\right)\theta^{-\frac{2}{3}-1} - 4{\cdot}4 \times \left(-\tfrac{1}{5}\right)\theta^{-\frac{1}{5}-1} \ ;$$

or, $\dfrac{dz}{d\theta} = -1{\cdot}2\theta^{-\frac{5}{3}} + 0{\cdot}88\theta^{-\frac{6}{5}}$;

or, $\dfrac{dz}{d\theta} = \dfrac{0{\cdot}88}{\sqrt[5]{\theta^6}} - \dfrac{1{\cdot}2}{\sqrt[3]{\theta^5}}$.

(4) Differentiate $v = (3t^2 - 1{\cdot}2t + 1)^3$.

A direct way of doing this will be explained later (see p. 57) ; but we can nevertheless manage it now without any difficulty.

Developing the cube, we get

$$v = 27t^6 - 32{\cdot}4t^5 + 39{\cdot}96t^4 - 23{\cdot}328t^3 + 13{\cdot}32t^2 - 3{\cdot}6t + 1 \ ;$$

hence $\dfrac{dv}{dt} = 162t^5 - 162t^4 + 159{\cdot}84t^3 - 69{\cdot}984t^2 + 26{\cdot}64t - 3{\cdot}6$.

(5) Differentiate $y = (2x - 3)(x + 1)^2$.

$$\begin{aligned}
\frac{dy}{dx} &= (2x - 3)\frac{d[(x+1)(x+1)]}{dx} + (x+1)^2\frac{d(2x-3)}{dx} \\
&= (2x - 3)\left[(x+1)\frac{d(x+1)}{dx} + (x+1)\frac{d(x+1)}{dx}\right] \\
&\qquad\qquad\qquad\qquad + (x+1)^2\frac{d(2x-3)}{dx} \\
&= 2(x+1)[(2x-3)+(x+1)] = 2(x+1)(3x-2) \ ;
\end{aligned}$$

or, more simply, multiply out and then differentiate.

(6) Differentiate $\quad y = 0 \cdot 5x^3(x-3)$.

$$\frac{dy}{dx} = 0 \cdot 5\left[x^3\frac{d(x-3)}{dx} + (x-3)\frac{d(x^3)}{dx} \right]$$
$$= 0 \cdot 5[x^3 + (x-3)\times 3x^2] = 2x^3 - 4 \cdot 5x^2.$$

Same remarks as for preceding example.

(7) Differentiate $\quad w = \left(\theta + \dfrac{1}{\theta}\right)\left(\sqrt{\theta} + \dfrac{1}{\sqrt{\theta}}\right).$
This may be written
$$w = (\theta + \theta^{-1})(\theta^{\frac{1}{2}} + \theta^{-\frac{1}{2}}).$$

$$\frac{dw}{d\theta} = (\theta + \theta^{-1})\frac{d(\theta^{\frac{1}{2}} + \theta^{-\frac{1}{2}})}{d\theta} + (\theta^{\frac{1}{2}} + \theta^{-\frac{1}{2}})\frac{d(\theta + \theta^{-1})}{d\theta}$$
$$= (\theta + \theta^{-1})(\tfrac{1}{2}\theta^{-\frac{1}{2}} - \tfrac{1}{2}\theta^{-\frac{3}{2}}) + (\theta^{\frac{1}{2}} + \theta^{-\frac{1}{2}})(1 - \theta^{-2})$$
$$= \tfrac{1}{2}(\theta^{\frac{1}{2}} + \theta^{-\frac{3}{2}} - \theta^{-\frac{1}{2}} - \theta^{-\frac{5}{2}}) + (\theta^{\frac{1}{2}} + \theta^{-\frac{1}{2}} - \theta^{-\frac{3}{2}} - \theta^{-\frac{5}{2}})$$
$$= \frac{3}{2}\left(\sqrt{\theta} - \frac{1}{\sqrt{\theta^5}}\right) + \frac{1}{2}\left(\frac{1}{\sqrt{\theta}} - \frac{1}{\sqrt{\theta^3}}\right).$$

This, again, could be obtained more simply by multiplying the two factors first, and differentiating afterwards. This is not, however, always possible ; see, for instance, p. 144, example 8, in which the rule for differentiating a product *must* be used.

(8) Differentiate $\quad y = \dfrac{a}{1 + a\sqrt{x} + a^2x}$

$$\frac{dy}{dx} = \frac{(1 + ax^{\frac{1}{2}} + a^2x)\times 0 - a\dfrac{d(1 + ax^{\frac{1}{2}} + a^2x)}{dx}}{(1 + a\sqrt{x} + a^2x)^2}$$
$$= -\frac{a(\tfrac{1}{2}ax^{-\frac{1}{2}} + a^2)}{(1 + ax^{\frac{1}{2}} + a^2x)^2}.$$

(9) Differentiate $\quad y = \dfrac{x^2}{x^2+1}.$

$$\frac{dy}{dx} = \frac{(x^2+1)2x - x^2\times 2x}{(x^2+1)^2} = \frac{2x}{(x^2+1)^2}.$$

(10) Differentiate $y = \dfrac{a + \sqrt{x}}{a - \sqrt{x}}$.

In the indexed form, $y = \dfrac{a + x^{\frac{1}{2}}}{a - x^{\frac{1}{2}}}$.

$$\frac{dy}{dx} = \frac{(a - x^{\frac{1}{2}})(\frac{1}{2}x^{-\frac{1}{2}}) - (a + x^{\frac{1}{2}})(-\frac{1}{2}x^{-\frac{1}{2}})}{(a - x^{\frac{1}{2}})^2} = \frac{a - x^{\frac{1}{2}} + a + x^{\frac{1}{2}}}{2(a - x^{\frac{1}{2}})^2 x^{\frac{1}{2}}};$$

hence $\qquad\qquad \dfrac{dy}{dx} = \dfrac{a}{(a - \sqrt{x})^2 \sqrt{x}}$.

(11) Differentiate $\theta = \dfrac{1 - a\sqrt[3]{t^2}}{1 + a\sqrt[2]{t^3}}$.

Now $\qquad\qquad \theta = \dfrac{1 - at^{\frac{2}{3}}}{1 + at^{\frac{3}{2}}}$.

$$\frac{d\theta}{dt} = \frac{(1 + at^{\frac{3}{2}})(-\frac{2}{3}at^{-\frac{1}{3}}) - (1 - at^{\frac{2}{3}}) \times \frac{3}{2}at^{\frac{1}{2}}}{(1 + at^{\frac{3}{2}})^2}$$

$$= \frac{5a^2\sqrt[6]{t^7} - \dfrac{4a}{\sqrt[3]{t}} - 9a\sqrt[2]{t}}{6(1 + a\sqrt[2]{t^3})^2}.$$

(12) A reservoir of square cross-section has sides sloping at an angle of 45° with the vertical. The side of the bottom is p feet in length, and water flows in the reservoir at the rate of c cubic feet per minute. Find an expression for the rate at which the surface of the water is rising at the instant its depth is h feet. Calculate this rate when $p = 17$, $h = 4$ and $c = 35$.

The volume of a frustum of pyramid of height H, and of bases A and a, is $V = \dfrac{H}{3}(A + a + \sqrt{Aa})$. It is easily seen that, the slope being 45°, for a depth of h, the length of the side of the upper square surface of water is $(p+2h)$ feet; thus $A = p^2$, $a = (p+2h)^2$ and the volume of the water is

$$\tfrac{1}{3}h\{p^2 + p(p+2h) + (p+2h)^2\} \text{ cubic feet}$$

$$= p^2h + 2ph^2 + \tfrac{4}{3}h^3 \text{ cubic feet.}$$

Now, if t be the time in minutes taken for this volume of water to flow in,

$$ct = p^2h + 2ph^2 + \tfrac{4}{3}h^3.$$

From this relation we have the rate at which h increases with t, that is $\dfrac{dh}{dt}$, but as the above expression is in the form, $t =$ function of h, rather than $h =$ function of t, it will be easier to find $\dfrac{dt}{dh}$ and then invert the result, for

$$\frac{dt}{dh} \times \frac{dh}{dt} = 1 \text{ (see pages 108 and 123).}$$

Hence, since c and p are constants, and

$$ct = p^2h + 2ph^2 + \tfrac{4}{3}h^3,$$

$$\therefore \ c\,\frac{dt}{dh} = p^2 + 4ph + 4h^2 = (p+2h)^2,$$

so that $\dfrac{dh}{dt} = \dfrac{c}{(p+2h)^2}$, which is the required expression.

When $p = 17$, $h = 4$ and $c = 35$; this becomes 0·056 feet per minute.

(13) The absolute pressure, in atmospheres, P, of saturated steam at the temperature $t°$ C. is given by Dulong as being $P = \left(\dfrac{40+t}{140}\right)^5$ as long as t is above 80°. Find the rate of variation of the pressure with the temperature at 100° C.

Since $\qquad P = \left(\dfrac{40+t}{140}\right)^5$; $\quad \dfrac{dP}{dt} = \dfrac{5(40+t)^4}{(140)^5}$, so that when $t = 100$,

$$\frac{dP}{dt} = \frac{5 \times (140)^4}{(140)^5} = \frac{5}{140} = \frac{1}{28} = 0 \cdot 036.$$

Thus, the rate of variation of the pressure is, when $t = 100$, $0 \cdot 036$ atmosphere per degree centigrade change of temperature.

EXERCISES III

(See page 240 for Answers)

(1) Differentiate

      (a) $u = 1 + x + \dfrac{x^2}{1 \times 2} + \dfrac{x^3}{1 \times 2 \times 3} + \cdots$.

      (b) $y = ax^2 + bx + c.$ (c) $y = (x + a)^2.$

      (d) $y = (x + a)^3.$

(2) If $w = at - \frac{1}{2}bt^2$, find $\dfrac{dw}{dt}$.

(3) Find the differential coefficient of

$$y = (x + \sqrt{-1}) \times (x - \sqrt{-1}).$$

(4) Differentiate

$$y = (197x - 34x^2) \times (7 + 22x - 83x^3).$$

(5) If $x = (y + 3) \times (y + 5)$, find $\dfrac{dx}{dy}$.

(6) Differentiate $y = 1 \cdot 3709x \times (112 \cdot 6 + 45 \cdot 202x^2).$

Find the differential coefficients of

(7) $y = \dfrac{2x + 3}{3x + 2}$.   (8) $y = \dfrac{1 + x + 2x^2 + 3x^3}{1 + x + 2x^2}$.

(9) $y = \dfrac{ax + b}{cx + d}$.   (10) $y = \dfrac{x^n + a}{x^{-n} + b}$.

(11) The temperature t of the filament of an incandescent electric lamp is connected to the current passing through the lamp by the relation

$$C = a + bt + ct^2.$$

Find an expression giving the variation of the current corresponding to a variation of temperature.

(12) The following formulae have been proposed to express the relation between the electric resistance R of a wire at the temperature $t°$ C., and the resistance R_0 of that same wire at $0°$ centigrade, a and b being constants.

$$R = R_0(1 + at + bt^2).$$
$$R = R_0(1 + at + b\sqrt{t}).$$
$$R = R_0(1 + at + bt^2)^{-1}.$$

Find the rate of variation of the resistance with regard to temperature as given by each of these formulae.

(13) The electromotive force E of a certain type of standard cell has been found to vary with the temperature t according to the relation

$$E = 1\cdot4340[1 - 0\cdot000814\,(t-15) + 0\cdot000007\,(t-15)^2]\ \text{volts}.$$

Find the change of electromotive force per degree, at $15°$, $20°$ and $25°$.

(14) The electromotive force necessary to maintain an electric arc of length l with a current of intensity i has been found by Mrs. Ayrton to be

$$E = a + bl + \frac{c + kl}{i},$$

where a, b, c, k are constants.

Find an expression for the variation of the electromotive force (a) with regard to the length of the arc ; (b) with regard to the strength of the current.

CHAPTER VII

SUCCESSIVE DIFFERENTIATION

LET us try the effect of repeating several times over the operation of differentiating a function (see p. 11). Begin with a concrete case.

Let $y = x^5$.

First differentiation, $5x^4$.

Second differentiation, $5 \times 4x^3$ $= 20x^3$.

Third differentiation, $5 \times 4 \times 3x^2$ $= 60x^2$.

Fourth differentiation, $5 \times 4 \times 3 \times 2x$ $= 120x$.

Fifth differentiation, $5 \times 4 \times 3 \times 2 \times 1 = 120$.

Sixth differentiation, $= 0$.

There is a certain notation, with which we are already acquainted (see p. 12), used by some writers, that is very convenient. This is to employ the general symbol $f(x)$ for any function of x. Here the symbol $f(\ )$ is read as " function of ", without saying what particular function is meant. So the statement $y = f(x)$ merely tells us that y is a function of x, it may be x^2 or ax^n, or cos x or any other complicated function of x.

The corresponding symbol for the differential coefficient is $f'(x)$, which is simpler to write than $\frac{dy}{dx}$. This is called the " derived function " of x.

Suppose we differentiate over again, we shall get the " second derived function " or second differential coefficient, which is denoted by $f''(x)$; and so on.

Now let us generalize.

42

Let $y = f(x) = x^n$.

First differentiation, $\qquad f'(x) = nx^{n-1}$.

Second differentiation, $\qquad f''(x) = n(n-1)x^{n-2}$.

Third differentiation, $\qquad f'''(x) = n(n-1)(n-2)x^{n-3}$.

Fourth differentiation, $f''''(x) = n(n-1)(n-2)(n-3)x^{n-4}$.

$$\text{etc., etc.}$$

But this is not the only way of indicating successive differentiations. For,

if the original function be $\qquad y = f(x)$;

once differentiating gives $\qquad \dfrac{dy}{dx} = f'(x)$;

twice differentiating gives $\qquad \dfrac{d\left(\frac{dy}{dx}\right)}{dx} = f''(x)$;

and this is more conveniently written as $\dfrac{d^2y}{(dx)^2}$, or more usually $\dfrac{d^2y}{dx^2}$. Similarly, we may write as the result of thrice differentiating, $\dfrac{d^3y}{dx^3} = f'''(x)$.

Examples.

Now let us try $\quad y = f(x) = 7x^4 + 3 \cdot 5x^3 - \frac{1}{2}x^2 + x - 2$.

$$\frac{dy}{dx} = f'(x) \quad = 28x^3 + 10 \cdot 5x^2 - x + 1,$$

$$\frac{d^2y}{dx^2} = f''(x) \quad = 84x^2 + 21x - 1,$$

$$\frac{d^3y}{dx^3} = f'''(x) \quad = 168x + 21.$$

$$\frac{d^4y}{dx^4} = f''''(x) = 168.$$

$$\frac{d^5y}{dx^5} = f'''''(x) = 0.$$

In a similar manner if $y = \phi(x) = 3x(x^2 - 4)$,

$$\phi'(x) = \frac{dy}{dx} = 3[x \times 2x + (x^2 - 4) \times 1] = 3(3x^2 - 4),$$

$$\phi''(x) = \frac{d^2y}{dx^2} = 3 \times 6x = 18x.$$

$$\phi'''(x) = \frac{d^3y}{dx^3} = 18,$$

$$\phi''''(x) = \frac{d^4y}{dx^4} = 0.$$

EXERCISES IV

(*See page* 241 *for Answers*)

Find $\frac{dy}{dx}$ and $\frac{d^2y}{dx^2}$ for the following expressions :

(1) $y = 17x + 12x^2$. (2) $y = \dfrac{x^2 + a}{x + a}$.

(3) $y = 1 + \dfrac{x}{1} + \dfrac{x^2}{1 \times 2} + \dfrac{x^3}{1 \times 2 \times 3} + \dfrac{x^4}{1 \times 2 \times 3 \times 4}$.

(4) Find the 2nd and 3rd derived functions in the Exercises III (p. 40), No. 1 to No. 7, and in the Examples given (p. 35), No. 1 to No. 7.

CHAPTER VIII

WHEN TIME VARIES

SOME of the most important problems of the calculus are those where time is the independent variable, and we have to think about the values of some other quantity that varies when the time varies. Some things grow larger as time goes on ; some other things grow smaller. The distance that a train has travelled from its starting place goes on ever increasing as time goes on. Trees grow taller as the years go by. Which is growing at the greater rate : a plant 12 inches high which in one month becomes 14 inches high, or a tree 12 feet high which in a year becomes 14 feet high?

In this chapter we are going to make much use of the word *rate*. Nothing to do with poor-rate, or police-rate (except that even here the word suggests a proportion—a ratio—so many pence in the pound). Nothing to do even with birth-rate or death-rate, though these words suggest so many births or deaths per thousand of the population. When a motor-car whizzes by us, we say : What a terrific rate! When a spend-thrift is flinging about his money, we remark that that young man is living at a prodigious rate. What do we mean by *rate*? In both these cases we are making a mental comparison of something that is happening, and the length of time it takes to happen. If the motor-car flies past us going 10 yards per second, a simple bit of mental arithmetic will show us that this is equivalent—while it lasts—to a rate of 600 yards per minute, or over 20 miles per hour.

Now in what sense is it true that a speed of 10 yards per second is the same as 600 yards per minute? Ten yards is not the same as 600 yards, nor is one second the same thing as one minute. What we mean by saying that the *rate* is the same, is this : that the proportion borne between distance passed over and time taken to pass over it, is the same in both cases.

Take another example. A man may have only a few pounds in his possession and yet be able to spend money at the rate of millions a year—provided he goes on spending money at that rate for a few minutes only. Suppose you hand a shilling over the counter to pay for some goods ; and suppose the operation lasts exactly one second. Then, during that brief operation, you are parting with your money at the rate of 1 shilling per second, which is the same rate as £3 per minute, or £180 per hour, or £4320 per day, or £1,576,800 per year! If you have £10 in your pocket, you can go on spending money at the rate of a million a year for just $5\frac{1}{4}$ minutes.

It is said that Sandy had not been in London above five minutes when " bang went saxpence ". If he were to spend money at that rate throughout a day of 12 hours, he would be spending 6 shillings an hour, or £3 12*s.* per day, or £21 12*s.* a week, not counting the Sawbath.

Now try to put some of these ideas into differential notation.

Let *y* in this case stand for money, and let *t* stand for time.

If you are spending money, and the amount you spend in a short time *dt* be called *dy*, the *rate* of spending it will be $\dfrac{dy}{dt}$; or, as regards saving, with a minus sign, as $-\dfrac{dy}{dt}$, because then *dy* is a *decrement*, not an increment. But money is not a good example for the calculus, because it generally comes and goes by jumps, not by a continuous flow—you may earn £200 a year, but it does not keep running in all day long in a thin stream ; it comes in only weekly, or monthly, or quarterly, in lumps : and your expenditure also goes out in sudden payments.

A more apt illustration of the idea of a rate is furnished by the speed of a moving body. From London (Euston station) to Liverpool is 200 miles. If a train leaves London at 7 o'clock, and reaches Liverpool at 11 o'clock, you know that, since it has travelled 200 miles in 4 hours, its average rate must have been 50 miles per hour; because $\frac{200}{4} = \frac{50}{1}$. Here you are really making a mental comparison between the distance passed over and the time taken to pass over it. You are dividing one by the other. If y is the whole distance, and t the whole time, clearly the average rate is $\frac{y}{t}$. Now the speed was not actually constant all the way: at starting, and during the slowing up at the end of the journey, the speed was less. Probably at some part, when running downhill, the speed was over 60 miles an hour. If, during any particular element of time dt, the corresponding element of distance passed over was dy, then at that part of the journey the speed was $\frac{dy}{dt}$. The *rate* at which one quantity (in the present instance, *distance*) is changing in relation to the other quantity (in this case, *time*) is properly expressed, then, by stating the differential coefficient of one with respect to the other. A *velocity*, scientifically expressed, is the rate at which a very small distance in any given direction is being passed over, and may therefore be written

$$v = \frac{dy}{dt}.$$

But if the velocity v is not uniform, then it must be either increasing or else decreasing. The rate at which a velocity is increasing is called the *acceleration*. If a moving body is, at any particular instant, gaining an additional velocity dv in an element of time dt, then the acceleration a at that instant may be written

$$a = \frac{dv}{dt}.$$

But since $v = \dfrac{dy}{dt}$,

$$\therefore \quad a = \frac{dv}{dt} = \frac{d}{dt}\left(\frac{dy}{dt}\right) ;$$

which is usually written $\quad a = \dfrac{d^2y}{dt^2}$;

or the acceleration is the second differential coefficient of the distance, with respect to time. Acceleration is expressed as a change of velocity in unit time, for instance, as being so many feet per second per second ; the notation used being feet $\div$ second^2.

When a railway train has just begun to move, its velocity v is small ; but it is rapidly gaining speed—it is being hurried up, or accelerated, by the effort of the engine. So its $\dfrac{d^2y}{dt^2}$ is large. When it has got up its top speed it is no longer being accelerated, so that then $\dfrac{d^2y}{dt^2}$ has fallen to zero. But when it nears its stopping place its speed begins to slow down ; may, indeed, slow down very quickly if the brakes are put on, and during this period of *deceleration* or slackening of pace, the value of $\dfrac{dv}{dt}$, that is, of $\dfrac{d^2y}{dt^2}$, will be negative.

To accelerate a mass m requires the continuous application of force. The force necessary to accelerate a mass is proportional to the mass, and it is also proportional to the acceleration which is being imparted. Hence we may write for the force f, the expression

$$f = ma ;$$

or

$$f = m\,\frac{dv}{dt} ;$$

or

$$f = m\,\frac{d^2y}{dt^2} .$$

The product of a mass by the speed at which it is going is called its *momentum,* and is in symbols mv. If we differentiate momentum with respect to time we shall get $\dfrac{d(mv)}{dt}$ for the rate of change of momentum. But, since m is a constant quantity, this may be written $m\dfrac{dv}{dt}$, which we see above is the same as f. That is to say, force may be expressed either as mass times acceleration, or as rate of change of momentum.

Again, if a force is employed to move something (against an equal and opposite counter-force), it does *work*; and the amount of work done is measured by the product of the force into the distance (in its own direction) through which its point of application moves forward. So if a force f moves forward through a length y, the work done (which we may call w) will be

$$w = f \times y \; ;$$

where we take f as a constant force. If the force varies at different parts of the range y, then we must find an expression for its value from point to point. If f be the force along the small element of length dy, the amount of work done will be $f \times dy$. But as dy is only an element of length, only an element of work will be done. If we write w for work, then an element of work will be dw; and we have

$$dw = f \times dy \; ;$$
which may be written
$$dw = ma \cdot dy \; ;$$
or
$$dw = m\frac{d^2y}{dt^2} \cdot dy \; ;$$
or
$$dw = m\frac{dv}{dt} \cdot dy.$$

Further, we may transpose the expression and write

$$\frac{dw}{dy} = f.$$

This gives us yet a third definition of *force* ; that if it is being used to produce a displacement in any direction, the force (in that direction) is equal to the rate at which work is being done per unit of length in that direction. In this last sentence the word *rate* is clearly not used in its time-sense, but in its meaning as ratio or proportion.

Sir Isaac Newton, who was (along with Leibnitz) an inventor of the methods of the calculus, regarded all quantities that were varying as *flowing* ; and the ratio which we nowadays call the differential coefficient he regarded as the rate of flowing, or the *fluxion* of the quantity in question. He did not use the notation of the dy and dx, and dt (this was due to Leibnitz), but had instead a notation of his own. If y was a quantity that varied, or " flowed ", then his symbol for its rate of variation (or " fluxion ") was $\dot{y}$. If x was the variable, then its fluxion was called $\dot{x}$. The dot over the letter indicated that it had been differentiated. But this notation does not tell us what is the independent variable with respect to which the differentiation has been effected. When we see $\dfrac{dy}{dt}$ we know that y is to be differentiated with respect to t. If we see $\dfrac{dy}{dx}$ we know that y is to be differentiated with respect to x. But if we see merely $\dot{y}$, we cannot tell without looking at the context whether this is to mean $\dfrac{dy}{dx}$ or $\dfrac{dy}{dt}$ or $\dfrac{dy}{dz}$, or what is the other variable. So, therefore, this fluxional notation is less informing than the differential notation, and has in consequence largely dropped out of use. But its simplicity gives it an advantage if only we will agree to use it for those cases exclusively where *time* is the independent variable. In that case $\dot{y}$ will mean $\dfrac{dy}{dt}$ and $\dot{u}$ will mean $\dfrac{du}{dt}$; and $\ddot{x}$ will mean $\dfrac{d^2x}{dt^2}$.

Adopting this fluxional notation we may write the mechanical equations considered in the paragraphs above, as follows :

distance	x,
velocity	$v = \dot{x}$,
acceleration	$a = \dot{v} = \ddot{x}$,
force	$f = m\dot{v} = m\ddot{x}$,
work	$w = x \times m\ddot{x}$.

Examples.

(1) A body moves so that the distance x (in feet), which it travels from a certain point O, is given by the relation

$$x = 0\cdot2t^2 + 10\cdot4,$$

where t is the time in seconds elapsed since a certain instant. Find the velocity and acceleration 5 seconds after the body began to move, and also find the corresponding values when the distance covered is 100 feet. Find also the average velocity during the first 10 seconds of its motion. (Suppose distances and motion to the right to be positive.)

Now $x = 0\cdot2t^2 + 10\cdot4,$

$$v = \dot{x} = \frac{dx}{dt} = 0\cdot4t \; ; \quad \text{and} \quad a = \ddot{x} = \frac{d^2x}{dt^2} = 0\cdot4 = \text{constant.}$$

When $t = 0$, $x = 10\cdot4$ and $v = 0$. The body started from a point $10\cdot4$ feet to the right of the point O ; and the time was reckoned from the instant the body started.

When $t = 5$, $v = 0\cdot4 \times 5 = 2$ ft./sec. ; $a = 0\cdot4$ ft./sec².

When $x = 100$, $100 = 0\cdot2t^2 + 10\cdot4$, or $t^2 = 448$,

and $t = 21\cdot17$ sec. ; $v = 0\cdot4 \times 21\cdot17 = 8\cdot468$ ft./sec.

When $t = 10$,

distance travelled $= 0\cdot2 \times 10^2 + 10\cdot4 - 10\cdot4 = 20$ ft.

Average velocity $= \frac{20}{10} = 2$ ft./sec.

(It is the same velocity as the velocity at the middle of the interval, $t = 5$; for, the acceleration being constant, the velocity has varied uniformly from zero when $t = 0$ to 4 ft./sec. when $t = 10$.)

(2) In the above problem let us suppose
$$x = 0{\cdot}2t^2 + 3t + 10{\cdot}4.$$
$$v = \dot{x} = \frac{dx}{dt} = 0{\cdot}4t + 3 \; ; \quad a = \ddot{x} = \frac{d^2x}{dt^2} = 0{\cdot}4 = \text{constant}.$$

When $t = 0$, $x = 10{\cdot}4$ and $v = 3$ ft./sec., the time is reckoned from the instant at which the body passed a point 10·4 ft. from the point O, its velocity being then already 3 ft./sec. To find the time elapsed since it began moving, let $v = 0$; then $0{\cdot}4t + 3 = 0$, $t = -\frac{3}{4} = -7{\cdot}5$ sec. The body began moving 7·5 sec. before time was begun to be observed; 5 seconds after this gives $t = -2{\cdot}5$ and $v = 0{\cdot}4 \times -2{\cdot}5 + 3 = 2$ ft./sec.

When $x = 100$ ft.,
$$100 = 0{\cdot}2t^2 + 3t + 10{\cdot}4 \; ; \quad \text{or} \quad t^2 + 15t - 448 = 0 \; ;$$
hence $\quad t = 14{\cdot}95$ sec., $v = 0{\cdot}4 \times 14{\cdot}95 + 3 = 8{\cdot}98$ ft./sec.

To find the distance travelled during the **first 10** seconds of the motion one must know how far the body was from the point O when it started.

When $t = -7{\cdot}5$,
$$x = 0{\cdot}2 \times (-7{\cdot}5)^2 - 3 \times 7{\cdot}5 + 10{\cdot}4 = -0{\cdot}85 \text{ ft.},$$
that is 0·85 ft. to the left of the point O.

Now, when $t = 2{\cdot}5$,
$$x = 0{\cdot}2 \times 2{\cdot}5^2 + 3 \times 2{\cdot}5 + 10{\cdot}4 = 19{\cdot}15.$$

So, in 10 seconds, the distance travelled was $19{\cdot}15 + 0{\cdot}85 = 20$ ft., and
$$\text{the average velocity} = \tfrac{20}{10} = 2 \text{ ft./sec.}$$

(3) Consider a similar problem when the distance is given by $x = 0{\cdot}2t^2 - 3t + 10{\cdot}4$. Then $v = 0{\cdot}4t - 3$, $a = 0{\cdot}4 = \text{constant}$. When $t = 0$, $x = 10{\cdot}4$ as before, and $v = -3$; so that the body

was moving in the direction opposite to its motion in the previous cases. As the acceleration is positive, however, we see that this velocity will decrease as time goes on, until it becomes zero, when $v = 0$ or $0.4t - 3 = 0$; or $t = +7.5$ sec. After this, the velocity becomes positive; and 5 seconds after the body started, $t = 12.5$, and

$$v = 0.4 \times 12.5 - 3 = 2 \text{ ft./sec.}$$

When $x = 100$,

$$100 = 0.2t^2 - 3t + 10.4, \text{ or } t^2 - 15t - 448 = 0,$$

and $\qquad t = 29.95$; $v = 0.4 \times 29.95 - 3 = 8.98$ ft./sec.

When v is zero, $x = 0.2 \times 7.5^2 - 3 \times 7.5 + 10.4 = -0.85$, informing us that the body moves back to 0.85 ft. beyond the point O before it stops. Ten seconds later $t = 17.5$ and

$$x = 0.2 \times 17.5^2 - 3 \times 17.5 + 10.4 = 19.15.$$

The distance travelled $= 0.85 + 19.15 = 20.0$, and the average velocity is again 2 ft./sec.

(4) Consider yet another problem of the same sort with $x = 0.2t^3 - 3t^2 + 10.4$; $v = 0.6t^2 - 6t$; $a = 1.2t - 6$. The acceleration is no more constant.

When $t = 0$, $x = 10.4$, $v = 0$, $a = -6$. The body is at rest, but just ready to move with a negative acceleration, that is, to gain a velocity towards the point O.

(5) If we have $x = 0.2t^3 - 3t + 10.4$, then $v = 0.6t^2 - 3$, and $a = 1.2t$.

When $t = 0$, $x = 10.4$; $v = -3$; $a = 0$.

The body is moving towards the point O with a velocity of 3 ft./sec., and just at that instant the velocity is uniform.

We see that the conditions of the motion can always be at once ascertained from the time-distance equation and its first and second derived functions. In the last two cases the mean velocity during the first 10 seconds and the velocity 5 seconds after the start will no more be the same, because the velocity is not increasing uniformly, the acceleration being no longer constant.

(6) The angle θ (in radians) turned through by a wheel is given by $\theta = 3 + 2t - 0 \cdot 1t^3$, where t is the time in seconds from a certain instant ; find the angular velocity ω and the angular acceleration α, (a) after 1 second ; (b) after it has performed one revolution. At what time is it at rest, and how many revolutions has it performed up to that instant?

Writing for the acceleration

$$\omega = \dot{\theta} = \frac{d\theta}{dt} = 2 - 0\cdot3t^2, \quad \alpha = \ddot{\theta} = \frac{d^2\theta}{dt^2} = -0\cdot6t.$$

When $t = 0$, $\theta = 3$; $\omega = 2$ rad./sec. ; $\alpha = 0$.
When $t = 1$, $\omega = 2 - 0\cdot3 = 1\cdot7$ rad./sec. ; $\alpha = -0\cdot6$ rad./sec².
This is a retardation ; the wheel is slowing down.

After 1 revolution

$$\theta = 2\pi = 6\cdot28 ; \quad 6\cdot28 = 3 + 2t - 0\cdot1t^3.$$

By plotting the graph, $\theta = 3 + 2t - 0\cdot1t^3$, we can get the value or values of t for which $\theta = 6\cdot28$; these are $2\cdot11$ and $3\cdot03$ (there is a third negative value).

When $t = 2\cdot11$,
$\theta = 6\cdot28$; $\omega = 2 - 1\cdot34 = 0\cdot66$ rad./sec. ;
$\alpha = -1\cdot27$ rad./sec².
When $t = 3\cdot03$,
$\theta = 6\cdot28$; $\omega = 2 - 2\cdot754 = -0\cdot754$ rad./sec. ;
$\alpha = -1\cdot82$ rad./sec².

The velocity is reversed. The wheel is evidently at rest between these two instants ; it is at rest when $\omega = 0$, that is when $0 = 2 - 0\cdot3t^2$, or when $t = 2\cdot58$ sec., it has performed

$$\frac{\theta}{2\pi} = \frac{3 + 2 \times 2\cdot58 - 0\cdot1 \times 2\cdot58^3}{6\cdot28} = 1\cdot025 \text{ revolutions.}$$

EXERCISES V

(See page 242 for Answers)

(1) If $y = a + bt^2 + ct^4$; find $\dfrac{dy}{dt}$ and $\dfrac{d^2y}{dt^2}$.

$$Ans. \quad \frac{dy}{dt} = 2bt + 4ct^3 \; ; \quad \frac{d^2y}{dt^2} = 2b + 12ct^2.$$

(2) A body falling freely in space describes in t seconds a space s, in feet, expressed by the equation $s = 16t^2$. Draw a curve showing the relation between s and t. Also determine the velocity of the body at the following times from its being let drop : $t = 2$ seconds ; $t = 4 \cdot 6$ seconds ; $t = 0 \cdot 01$ second.

(3) If $x = at - \frac{1}{2}gt^2$; find $\dot{x}$ and $\ddot{x}$.

(4) If a body move according to the law

$$s = 12 - 4 \cdot 5t + 6 \cdot 2t^2,$$

find its velocity when $t = 4$ seconds ; s being in feet.

(5) Find the acceleration of the body mentioned in the preceding example. Is the acceleration the same for all values of t?

(6) The angle θ (in radians) turned through by a revolving wheel is connected with the time t (in seconds) that has elapsed since starting, by the law

$$\theta = 2 \cdot 1 - 3 \cdot 2t + 4 \cdot 8t^2.$$

Find the angular velocity (in radians per second) of that wheel when $1\frac{1}{2}$ seconds have elapsed. Find also its angular acceleration.

(7) A slider moves so that, during the first part of its motion, its distance s in inches from its starting point is given by the expression

$$s = 6 \cdot 8t^3 - 10 \cdot 8t \; ; \quad t \text{ being in seconds.}$$

Find the expression for the velocity and the acceleration at any time ; and hence find the velocity and the acceleration after 3 seconds.

(8) The motion of a rising balloon is such that its height h, in miles, is given at any instant by the expression

$$h = 0{\cdot}5 + \tfrac{1}{10}\sqrt[3]{t - 125} \; ; \; t \text{ being in seconds.}$$

Find an expression for the velocity and the acceleration at any time. Draw curves to show the variation of height, velocity and acceleration during the first ten minutes of the ascent.

(9) A stone is thrown downwards into water and its depth p in metres at any instant t seconds after reaching the surface of the water is given by the expression

$$p = \frac{4}{4 + t^2} + 0{\cdot}8t - 1.$$

Find an expression for the velocity and the acceleration at any time. Find the velocity and acceleration after 10 seconds.

(10) A body moves in such a way that the space described in the time t from starting is given by $s = t^n$, where n is a constant. Find the value of n when the velocity is doubled from the 5th to the 10th second ; find it also when the velocity is numerically equal to the acceleration at the end of the 10th second.

CHAPTER IX

INTRODUCING A USEFUL DODGE

SOMETIMES one is stumped by finding that the expression to be differentiated is too complicated to tackle directly.

Thus, the equation

$$y = (x^2 + a^2)^{\frac{3}{2}}$$

is awkward to a beginner.

Now the dodge to turn the difficulty is this: Write some symbol, such as u, for the expression $x^2 + a^2$; then the equation becomes

$$y = u^{\frac{3}{2}},$$

which you can easily manage; for

$$\frac{dy}{du} = \frac{3}{2} u^{\frac{1}{2}}.$$

Then tackle the expression

$$u = x^2 + a^2,$$

and differentiate it with respect to x

$$\frac{du}{dx} = 2x.$$

Then all that remains is plain sailing;

for
$$\frac{dy}{dx} = \frac{dy}{du} \times \frac{du}{dx};$$

that is,
$$\frac{dy}{dx} = \frac{3}{2} u^{\frac{1}{2}} \times 2x$$
$$= \tfrac{3}{2} (x^2 + a^2)^{\frac{1}{2}} \times 2x$$
$$= 3x (x^2 + a^2)^{\frac{1}{2}}:$$

and so the trick is done.

By and by, when you have learned how to deal with sines, and cosines, and exponentials, you will find this dodge of increasing usefulness.

Examples.

Let us practise this dodge on a few examples.

(1) Differentiate $y = \sqrt{a+x}$.

Let $u = a + x$.

$$\frac{du}{dx} = 1 \; ; \quad y = u^{\frac{1}{2}} \; ; \quad \frac{dy}{du} = \tfrac{1}{2} u^{-\frac{1}{2}} = \tfrac{1}{2}(a+x)^{-\frac{1}{2}}.$$

$$\frac{dy}{dx} = \frac{dy}{du} \times \frac{du}{dx} = \frac{1}{2\sqrt{a+x}} .$$

(2) Differentiate $y = \dfrac{1}{\sqrt{a+x^2}}$.

Let $u = a + x^2$.

$$\frac{du}{dx} = 2x \; ; \quad y = u^{-\frac{1}{2}} \; ; \quad \frac{dy}{du} = -\tfrac{1}{2} u^{-\frac{3}{2}}.$$

$$\frac{dy}{dx} = \frac{dy}{du} \times \frac{du}{dx} = -\frac{x}{\sqrt{(a+x^2)^3}} .$$

(3) Differentiate $y = \left(m - nx^{\frac{2}{3}} + \dfrac{p}{x^{\frac{4}{3}}} \right)^a$.

Let $u = m - nx^{\frac{2}{3}} + px^{-\frac{4}{3}}$.

$$\frac{du}{dx} = -\tfrac{2}{3} nx^{-\frac{1}{3}} - \tfrac{4}{3} px^{-\frac{7}{3}} \; ;$$

$$y = u^a \; ; \quad \frac{dy}{du} = au^{a-1}.$$

$$\frac{dy}{dx} = \frac{dy}{du} \times \frac{du}{dx} = -a \left(m - nx^{\frac{2}{3}} + \frac{p}{x^{\frac{4}{3}}} \right)^{a-1} (\tfrac{2}{3} nx^{-\frac{1}{3}} + \tfrac{4}{3} px^{-\mathbf{r}}).$$

(4) Differentiate $y = \dfrac{1}{\sqrt{x^3 - a^2}}$.

Let $u = x^3 - a^2$.

$$\frac{du}{dx} = 3x^2 \; ; \;\; y = u^{-\frac{1}{2}} \; ; \;\; \frac{dy}{du} = -\tfrac{1}{2}(x^3 - a^2)^{-\frac{3}{2}}.$$

$$\frac{dy}{dx} = \frac{dy}{du} \times \frac{du}{dx} = -\frac{3x^2}{2\sqrt{(x^3 - a^2)^3}}.$$

(5) Differentiate $y = \sqrt{\dfrac{1-x}{1+x}}$.

Write this as $\quad y = \dfrac{(1-x)^{\frac{1}{2}}}{(1+x)^{\frac{1}{2}}}$.

$$\frac{dy}{dx} = \frac{(1+x)^{\frac{1}{2}} \dfrac{d(1-x)^{\frac{1}{2}}}{dx} - (1-x)^{\frac{1}{2}} \dfrac{d(1+x)^{\frac{1}{2}}}{dx}}{1+x}$$

(We may also write $y = (1-x)^{\frac{1}{2}}(1+x)^{-\frac{1}{2}}$ and differentiate as a product.)

Proceeding as in exercise (1) above, we get

$$\frac{d(1-x)^{\frac{1}{2}}}{dx} = -\frac{1}{2\sqrt{1-x}} \; ; \quad \text{and} \quad \frac{d(1+x)^{\frac{1}{2}}}{dx} = \frac{1}{2\sqrt{1+x}}.$$

Hence $\quad \dfrac{dy}{dx} = -\dfrac{(1+x)^{\frac{1}{2}}}{2(1+x)\sqrt{1-x}} - \dfrac{(1-x)^{\frac{1}{2}}}{2(1+x)\sqrt{1+x}}$

$$= -\frac{1}{2\sqrt{1+x}\sqrt{1-x}} - \frac{\sqrt{1-x}}{2\sqrt{(1+x)^3}} \; ;$$

or $\quad \dfrac{dy}{dx} = -\dfrac{1}{(1+x)\sqrt{1-x^2}}$.

c

(6) Differentiate $y = \sqrt{\dfrac{x^3}{1+x^2}}$.

We may write this

$$y = x^{\frac{3}{2}}(1+x^2)^{-\frac{1}{2}} \; ;$$

$$\frac{dy}{dx} = \tfrac{3}{2}x^{\frac{1}{2}}(1+x^2)^{-\frac{1}{2}} + x^{\frac{3}{2}} \times \frac{d[(1+x^2)^{-\frac{1}{2}}]}{dx}.$$

Differentiating $(1+x^2)^{-\frac{1}{2}}$, as shown in exercise (2) above, we get

$$\frac{d[(1+x^2)^{-\frac{1}{2}}]}{dx} = -\frac{x}{\sqrt{(1+x^2)^3}} \; ;$$

so that $\quad \dfrac{dy}{dx} = \dfrac{3\sqrt{x}}{2\sqrt{1+x^2}} - \dfrac{\sqrt{x^5}}{\sqrt{(1+x^2)^3}} = \dfrac{\sqrt{x}\,(3+x^2)}{2\sqrt{(1+x^2)^3}}.$

(7) Differentiate $y = (x + \sqrt{x^2+x+a})^3$.

Let $u = x + \sqrt{x^2+x+a}$.

$$\frac{du}{dx} = 1 + \frac{d[(x^2+x+a)^{\frac{1}{2}}]}{dx}.$$

$$y = u^3 \; ; \quad \text{and} \; \frac{dy}{du} = 3u^2 = 3(x + \sqrt{x^2+x+a})^2.$$

Now let $\quad v = (x^2+x+a)^{\frac{1}{2}} \quad$ and $\quad w = (x^2+x+a).$

$$\frac{dw}{dx} = 2x+1 \; ; \quad v = w^{\frac{1}{2}} \; ; \quad \frac{dv}{dw} = \tfrac{1}{2}w^{-\frac{1}{2}}.$$

$$\frac{dv}{dx} = \frac{dv}{dw} \times \frac{dw}{dx} = \tfrac{1}{2}(x^2+x+a)^{-\frac{1}{2}}(2x+1).$$

Hence $\quad \dfrac{du}{dx} = 1 + \dfrac{2x+1}{2\sqrt{x^2+x+a}},$

$$\frac{dy}{dx} = \frac{dy}{du} \times \frac{du}{dx}$$

$$= 3(x + \sqrt{x^2+x+a})^2 \left(1 + \frac{2x+1}{2\sqrt{x^2+x+a}}\right).$$

(8) Differentiate $\quad y = \sqrt{\dfrac{a^2 + x^2}{a^2 - x^2}} \sqrt[3]{\dfrac{a^2 - x^2}{a^2 + x^2}}.$

We get $\quad y = \dfrac{(a^2 + x^2)^{\frac{1}{2}} (a^2 - x^2)^{\frac{1}{3}}}{(a^2 - x^2)^{\frac{1}{2}} (a^2 + x^2)^{\frac{1}{3}}} = (a^2 + x^2)^{\frac{1}{6}} (a^2 - x^2)^{-\frac{1}{6}}.$

$$\frac{dy}{dx} = (a^2 + x^2)^{\frac{1}{6}} \frac{d[(a^2 - x^2)^{-\frac{1}{6}}]}{dx} + \frac{d[(a^2 + x^2)^{\frac{1}{6}}]}{(a^2 - x^2)^{\frac{1}{6}} dx}.$$

Let $\quad u = (a^2 - x^2)^{-\frac{1}{6}} \quad$ and $\quad v = (a^2 - x^2).$

$$u = v^{-\frac{1}{6}} ; \quad \frac{du}{dv} = -\frac{1}{6} v^{-\frac{7}{6}} ; \quad \frac{dv}{dx} = -2x.$$

$$\frac{du}{dx} = \frac{du}{dv} \times \frac{dv}{dx} = \frac{1}{3} x (a^2 - x^2)^{-\frac{7}{6}}.$$

Let $\quad w = (a^2 + x^2)^{\frac{1}{6}} \quad$ and $\quad z = (a^2 + x^2).$

$$w = z^{\frac{1}{6}} ; \quad \frac{dw}{dz} = \frac{1}{6} z^{-\frac{5}{6}} ; \quad \frac{dz}{dx} = 2x.$$

$$\frac{dw}{dx} = \frac{dw}{dz} \times \frac{dz}{dx} = \frac{1}{3} x (a^2 + x^2)^{-\frac{5}{6}}.$$

Hence $\quad \dfrac{dy}{dx} = (a^2 + x^2)^{\frac{1}{6}} \dfrac{x}{3 (a^2 - x^2)^{\frac{7}{6}}} + \dfrac{x}{3 (a^2 - x^2)^{\frac{1}{6}} (a^2 + x^2)^{\frac{5}{6}}} ;$

or $\quad \dfrac{dy}{dx} = \dfrac{x}{3} \left[\sqrt[6]{\dfrac{a^2 + x^2}{(a^2 - x^2)^7}} + \dfrac{1}{\sqrt[6]{(a^2 - x^2)(a^2 + x^2)^5}} \right].$

(9) Differentiate y^n with respect to y^5.

$$\frac{d(y^n)}{d(y^5)} = \frac{ny^{n-1}}{5y^{5-1}} = \frac{n}{5} y^{n-5}.$$

(10) Find the first and second differential coefficients of
$y = \dfrac{x}{b} \sqrt{(a - x)x}.$

$$\frac{dy}{dx} = \frac{x}{b} \frac{d\{[(a - x)x]^{\frac{1}{2}}\}}{dx} + \frac{\sqrt{(a - x)x}}{b}.$$

Let $u = [(a-x)x]^{\frac{1}{2}}$ and let $w = (a-x)x$; then $u = w^{\frac{1}{2}}$.

$$\frac{du}{dw} = \frac{1}{2} w^{-\frac{1}{2}} = \frac{1}{2w^{\frac{1}{2}}} = \frac{1}{2\sqrt{(a-x)x}}.$$

$$\frac{dw}{dx} = a - 2x.$$

$$\frac{du}{dw} \times \frac{dw}{dx} = \frac{du}{dx} = \frac{a-2x}{2\sqrt{(a-x)x}}.$$

Hence
$$\frac{dy}{dx} = \frac{x(a-2x)}{2b\sqrt{(a-x)x}} + \frac{\sqrt{(a-x)x}}{b} = \frac{x(3a-4x)}{2b\sqrt{(a-x)x}}.$$

Now
$$\frac{d^2y}{dx^2} = \frac{2b\sqrt{(a-x)x}\,(3a-8x) - \dfrac{(3ax-4x^2)\,b\,(a-2x)}{\sqrt{(a-x)x}}}{4b^2(a-x)x}$$

$$= \frac{3a^2 - 12ax + 8x^2}{4b(a-x)\sqrt{(a-x)x}}.$$

(We shall need these two last differential coefficients later on. See Ex. X, No. 11.)

EXERCISES VI

(See page 242 for Answers)

Differentiate the following :

(1) $y = \sqrt{x^2 + 1}$.

(2) $y = \sqrt{x^2 + a^2}$.

(3) $y = \dfrac{1}{\sqrt{a+x}}$.

(4) $y = \dfrac{a}{\sqrt{a-x^2}}$.

(5) $y = \dfrac{\sqrt{x^2-a^2}}{x^2}$.

(6) $y = \dfrac{\sqrt[3]{x^4+a}}{\sqrt[2]{x^3+a}}$.

(7) $y = \dfrac{a^2+x^2}{(a+x)^2}$.

(8) Differentiate y^5 with respect to y^2.

(9) Differentiate $y = \dfrac{\sqrt{1-\theta^2}}{1-\theta}$.

The process can be extended to three or more differential coefficients, so that $\dfrac{dy}{dx} = \dfrac{dy}{dz} \times \dfrac{dz}{dv} \times \dfrac{dv}{dx}$.

Examples.

(1) If $z = 3x^4$; $v = \dfrac{7}{z^2}$; $y = \sqrt{1+v}$, find $\dfrac{dy}{dx}$.

We have $\dfrac{dy}{dv} = \dfrac{1}{2\sqrt{1+v}}$; $\dfrac{dv}{dz} = -\dfrac{14}{z^3}$; $\dfrac{dz}{dx} = 12x^3$.

$$\dfrac{dy}{dx} = -\dfrac{168x^3}{(2\sqrt{1+v})z^3} = -\dfrac{28}{3x^5\sqrt{9x^8+7}}.$$

(2) If $t = \dfrac{1}{5\sqrt{\theta}}$; $x = t^3 + \dfrac{t}{2}$; $v = \dfrac{7x^2}{\sqrt[3]{x-1}}$, find $\dfrac{dv}{d\theta}$.

$$\dfrac{dv}{dx} = \dfrac{7x(5x-6)}{3\sqrt[3]{(x-1)^4}} ; \quad \dfrac{dx}{dt} = 3t^2 + \tfrac{1}{2} ; \quad \dfrac{dt}{d\theta} = -\dfrac{1}{10\sqrt{\theta^3}}.$$

Hence $\dfrac{dv}{d\theta} = -\dfrac{7x(5x-6)(3t^2+\tfrac{1}{2})}{30\sqrt[3]{(x-1)^4}\sqrt{\theta^3}}$,

an expression in which x must be replaced by its value, and t by its value in terms of θ.

(3) If $\theta = \dfrac{3a^2x}{\sqrt{x^3}}$; $\omega = \dfrac{\sqrt{1-\theta^2}}{1+\theta}$; and $\phi = \sqrt{3} - \dfrac{1}{\omega\sqrt{2}}$, find $\dfrac{d\phi}{dx}$.

We get $\theta = 3a^2x^{-\frac{1}{2}}$; $\omega = \sqrt{\dfrac{1-\theta}{1+\theta}}$; and $\phi = \sqrt{3} - \dfrac{1}{\sqrt{2}}\,\omega^{-1}$.

$$\dfrac{d\theta}{dx} = -\dfrac{3a^2}{2\sqrt{x^3}} ; \quad \dfrac{d\omega}{d\theta} = -\dfrac{1}{(1+\theta)\sqrt{1-\theta^2}},$$

(see example 5, p. 59) ; and

$$\dfrac{d\phi}{d\omega} = \dfrac{1}{\sqrt{2}\,.\,\omega}.$$

So that $\dfrac{d\phi}{dx} = \dfrac{1}{\sqrt{2}\times\omega^2} \times \dfrac{1}{(1+\theta)\sqrt{1-\theta^2}} \times \dfrac{3a^2}{2\sqrt{x^3}}.$

Replace now first ω, then θ by its value.

EXERCISES VII

(*See page 242 for Answers*)

You can now successfully try the following.

(1) If $u = \frac{1}{2}x^3$; $v = 3(u + u^2)$; and $w = \dfrac{1}{v^2}$, find $\dfrac{dw}{dx}$.

(2) If $y = 3x^2 + \sqrt{2}$; $z = \sqrt{1 + y}$; and $v = \dfrac{1}{\sqrt{3 + 4z}}$, find $\dfrac{dv}{dx}$.

(3) If $y = \dfrac{x^3}{\sqrt{3}}$; $z = (1 + y)^2$; and $u = \dfrac{1}{\sqrt{1 + z}}$, find $\dfrac{du}{dx}$.

The following exercises are placed here for reasons of space and because their solution depends upon the dodge explained in the foregoing chapter, but they should not be attempted until Chapters XIV and XV (pp. 111–44) have been read.

(4) If $y = 2a^3 \log_\epsilon u - u(5a^2 - 2au + \frac{1}{3}u^2)$, and $u = a + x$,

show that $$\frac{dy}{dx} = \frac{x^2(a - x)}{a + x}.$$

(5) For the curve $x = a(\theta - \sin \theta)$, $y = a(1 - \cos \theta)$, find $\dfrac{dx}{d\theta}$ and $\dfrac{dy}{d\theta}$; hence deduce the value of $\dfrac{dy}{dx}$.

(6) Find $\dfrac{dx}{d\theta}$ and $\dfrac{dy}{d\theta}$ for the curve $x = a \cos^3\theta$, $y = a \sin^3\theta$; hence obtain $\dfrac{dy}{dx}$.

(7) Given that $y = \log_\epsilon \sin (x^2 - a^2)$, find $\dfrac{dy}{dx}$ in its simplest form.

(8) If $u = x + y$ and $4x = 2u - \log_\epsilon (2u - 1)$, show that

$$\frac{dy}{dx} = \frac{x + y}{x + y - 1}.$$

CHAPTER X

GEOMETRICAL MEANING OF DIFFERENTIATION

IT is useful to consider what geometrical meaning can be given to the differential coefficient.

In the first place, any function of x, such, for example, as x^2, or $\sqrt{x}$, or $ax + b$, can be plotted as a curve; and nowadays every schoolboy is familiar with the process of curve-plotting.

Let PQR, in Fig. 7, be a portion of a curve plotted with respect to the axes of coordinates OX and OY. Consider any point Q on this curve, where the abscissa of the point is x and its ordinate is y. Now observe how y changes when x is varied. If x is made to increase by a small increment dx, to the right, it will be observed that y also (in *this* particular curve) increases

FIG. 7.

by a small increment dy (because this particular curve happens to be an *ascending* curve). Then the ratio of dy to dx is a measure of the degree to which the curve is sloping up between the two points Q and T. As a matter of fact, it can be seen on the figure that the curve between Q and T has many different slopes, so that we cannot very well speak of the slope of the curve between Q and T. If, however, Q and T are so near each other that the small portion QT of the curve is practically straight, then it is true to say that the ratio $\dfrac{dy}{dx}$ is the slope of the curve along QT. The straight line

QT produced on either side touches the curve along the portion *QT* only, and if this portion is indefinitely small, the straight line will touch the curve at practically one point only, and be therefore a *tangent* to the curve.

This tangent to the curve has evidently the same slope as *QT*, so that $\frac{dy}{dx}$ is the slope of the tangent to the curve at the point *Q* for which the value of $\frac{dy}{dx}$ is found.

We have seen that the short expression " the slope of a curve " has no precise meaning, because a curve has so many slopes—in fact, every small portion of a curve has a different slope. " The slope of a curve *at a point* " is, however, a perfectly defined thing ; it is the slope of a very small portion of the curve situated just at that point ; and we have seen that this is the same as " the slope of the tangent to the curve at that point ".

Observe that *dx* is a short step to the right, and *dy* the corresponding short step upwards. These steps must be considered as short as possible—in fact indefinitely short,— though in diagrams we have to represent them by bits that are not infinitesimally small, otherwise they could not be seen.

We shall hereafter make considerable use of this circumstance that $\frac{dy}{dx}$ represents the slope of the tangent to the curve at any point.

FIG. 8.

It is usual to confine the word *slope* to the angle θ made by the tangent at any point on curve with the *x*-axis, while $\frac{dy}{dx}$, which is equal to $\tan \theta$, is called the *gradient* of the curve at the point.

If a curve is sloping up at 45° at a particular point, as in Fig. 8, dy and dx will be equal, and the value of $\frac{dy}{dx} = 1$.

If the curve slopes up steeper than 45° (Fig. 9), $\frac{dy}{dx}$ will be greater than 1.

If the curve slopes up very gently, as in Fig. 10, $\frac{dy}{dx}$ will be a fraction smaller than 1.

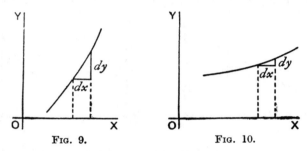

Fig. 9.   Fig. 10.

For a horizontal line, or a horizontal place in a curve, $dy = 0$, and therefore $\frac{dy}{dx} = 0$.

If a curve slopes *downward*, as in Fig. 11, dy will be a step down, and must therefore be reckoned of negative value; hence $\frac{dy}{dx}$ will have negative sign also

Fig. 11.

If the " curve " happens to be a straight line, like that in Fig. 12, the value of $\dfrac{dy}{dx}$ will be the same at all points along it. In other words its *slope* is constant.

If a curve is one that turns more upwards as it goes along to the right, the values of $\dfrac{dy}{dx}$ will become greater and greater with the increasing steepness, as in Fig. 13.

FIG. 12.   FIG. 13.

If a curve is one that gets flatter and flatter as it goes along, the values of $\dfrac{dy}{dx}$ will become smaller and smaller as the flatter part is reached, as in Fig. 14.

If a curve first descends, and then goes up again, as in Fig. 15, presenting a concavity upwards, then clearly $\dfrac{dy}{dx}$ will first

FIG. 14.

FIG. 15.

be negative, with diminishing values as the curve flattens, then will be zero at the point where the bottom of the trough of the curve is reached ; and from this point onward $\frac{dy}{dx}$ will have positive values that go on increasing. In such a case y is said to pass through a *minimum*. The minimum value of y is not necessarily the smallest value of y, it is that value of y corresponding to the bottom of the trough ; for instance, in Fig. 28 (p. 85), the value of y corresponding to the bottom of the trough is 1, while y takes elsewhere values which are smaller than this. The characteristic of a minimum is that y must increase *on either side* of it.

N.B.—For the particular value of x that makes y *a minimum*, the value of $\frac{dy}{dx} = 0$.

If a curve first ascends and then descends, the values of $\frac{dy}{dx}$ will be positive at first ; then zero, as the summit is reached ; then negative, as the curve slopes downwards, as in Fig. 16.

Fig. 16.

In this case y is said to pass through a *maximum*, but the maximum value of y is not necessarily the greatest value of y. In Fig. 28, the maximum of y is $2\frac{1}{3}$, but this is by no means the greatest value y can have at some other point of the curve.

N.B.—For the particular value of x that makes y *a maximum,* the value of $\frac{dy}{dx} = 0$.

If a curve has the particular form of Fig. 17, the values of $\frac{dy}{dx}$ will always be positive ; but there will be one particular place where the slope is least steep, where the value of $\frac{dy}{dx}$ will be a minimum ; that is, less than it is at any other part of the curve.

If a curve has the form of Fig. 18, the value of $\frac{dy}{dx}$ will be negative in the upper part, and positive in the lower part ;

FIG. 17.   FIG. 18.

while. at the nose of the curve where it becomes actually perpendicular, the value of $\frac{dy}{dx}$ will be infinitely great.

Now that we understand that $\frac{dy}{dx}$ measures the steepness of a curve at any point, let us turn to some of the equations which we have already learned how to differentiate.

(1) As the simplest case take this :

$$y = x + b.$$

It is plotted out in Fig. 19, using equal scales for x and y.
If we put $x=0$, then the corresponding ordinate will be $y=b$;
that is to say, the " curve " crosses the y-axis at the height b.
From here it ascends at 45°; for whatever values we give to
x to the right, we have an equal y to ascend. The line has a
gradient of 1 in 1.

Now differentiate $y=x+b$, by the rules we have already
learned (pp. 18 and 22 *ante*), and we get $\frac{dy}{dx}=1$.

FIG. 19.

FIG. 20.

The slope of the line is such that for every little step dx to
the right, we go an equal little step dy upward. And this slope
is constant—always the same slope.

(2) Take another case :

$$y=ax+b.$$

We know that this curve, like the preceding one, will start
from a height b on the y-axis. But before we draw the curve,

let us find its slope by differentiating ; which gives us $\frac{dy}{dx}=a$.

The slope will be constant, at an angle, the tangent of which is
here called a. Let us assign to a some numerical value—say $\frac{1}{3}$.

Then we must give it such a slope that
it ascends 1 in 3 ; or dx will be 3 times
as great as dy ; as magnified in Fig. 21.
So, draw the line in Fig. 20 at this slope.

FIG. 21.

(3) Now for a slightly harder case.

Let $\qquad\qquad y = ax^2 + b.$

Again the curve will start on the y-axis at a height b above the origin.

Now differentiate. [If you have forgotten, turn back to p. 22; or, rather, *don't* turn back, but think out the differentiation.]

$$\frac{dy}{dx} = 2ax.$$

This shows that the steepness will not be constant : it increases as x increases. At the starting point P, where $x = 0$, the curve (Fig. 22) has no steepness—that is, it is level. On

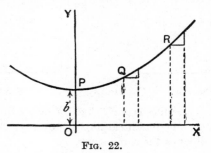

Fig. 22.

the left of the origin, where x has negative values, $\dfrac{dy}{dx}$ will also have negative values, or will descend from left to right, as in the Figure.

Let us illustrate this by working out a particular instance. Taking the equation

$$y = \tfrac{1}{4}x^2 + 3,$$

and differentiating it, we get

$$\frac{dy}{dx} = \tfrac{1}{2}x.$$

Now assign a few successive values, say from 0 to 5, to x; and calculate the corresponding values of y by the first equation ; and of $\dfrac{dy}{dx}$ from the second equation. Tabulating results, we have :

x	0	1	2	3	4	5
y	3	$3\frac{1}{4}$	4	$5\frac{1}{4}$	7	$9\frac{1}{4}$
$\dfrac{dy}{dx}$	0	$\frac{1}{2}$	1	$1\frac{1}{2}$	2	$2\frac{1}{2}$

Then plot them out in two curves, Figs. 23 and 24 ; in Fig. 23 plotting the values of y against those of x, and in Fig. 24 those

FIG. 23.

FIG. 24.

of $\dfrac{dy}{dx}$ against those of x. For any assigned value of x, the

height of the ordinate in the second curve is proportional to the *slope* of the first curve.

If a curve comes to a sudden *cusp*, as in Fig. 25, the slope at that point suddenly changes from a slope upward to a slope down-ward. In that case $\dfrac{dy}{dx}$ will clearly undergo an abrupt change from a positive to a negative value.

FIG. 25.

The following examples show further applications of the principles just explained.

(4) Find the slope of the tangent to the curve $y = \dfrac{1}{2x} + 3$, at the point where $x = -1$. Find the angle which this tangent makes with the curve $y = 2x^2 + 2$.

The slope of the tangent is the slope of the curve at the point where they touch one another (see pp. 65–6); that is, it is the $\dfrac{dy}{dx}$ of the curve for that point. Here $\dfrac{dy}{dx} = -\dfrac{1}{2x^2}$ and for $x = -1$, $\dfrac{dy}{dx} = -\dfrac{1}{2}$, which is the slope of the tangent and of the curve at that point. The tangent, being a straight line, has for equation $y = ax + b$, and its slope is $\dfrac{dy}{dx} = a$, hence $a = -\dfrac{1}{2}$. Also if $x = -1$, $y = \dfrac{1}{2(-1)} + 3 = 2\frac{1}{2}$; and as the tangent passes by this point, the coordinates of the point must satisfy the equation of the tangent, namely

$$y = -\frac{1}{2}x + b,$$

so that $2\frac{1}{2} = -\dfrac{1}{2} \times (-1) + b$ and $b = 2$; the equation of the tangent is therefore $y = -\dfrac{1}{2}x + 2$.

Now, when two curves meet, the intersection being a point common to both curves, its coordinates must satisfy the equation of each one of the two curves; that is, it must be a solution of the system of simultaneous equations formed by coupling together the equations of the curves. Here the curves meet one another at points given by the solution of

$$\begin{cases} y = 2x^2 + 2, \\ y = -\frac{1}{2}x + 2 \end{cases} \quad \text{or} \quad 2x^2 + 2 = -\tfrac{1}{2}x + 2;$$

that is,
$$x(2x + \tfrac{1}{2}) = 0.$$

This equation has for its solutions $x = 0$ and $x = -\frac{1}{4}$. The slope of the curve $y = 2x^2 + 2$ at any point is

$$\frac{dy}{dx} = 4x.$$

For the point where $x = 0$, this slope is zero ; the curve is horizontal. For the point where

$$x = -\frac{1}{4}, \quad \frac{dy}{dx} = -1 ;$$

hence the curve at that point slopes downwards to the right at such an angle θ with the horizontal that $\tan \theta = 1$; that is, at $45°$ to the horizontal.

The slope of the straight line is $-\frac{1}{2}$; that is, it slopes downwards to the right and makes with the horizontal an angle ϕ such that $\tan \phi = \frac{1}{2}$; that is, an angle of $26° 34'$. It follows that at the first point the curve cuts the straight line at an angle of $26° 34'$, while at the second it cuts it at an angle of $45° - 26° 34' = 18° 26'$.

(5) A straight line is to be drawn, through a point whose coordinates are $x = 2$, $y = -1$, as tangent to the curve

$$y = x^2 - 5x + 6.$$

Find the coordinates of the point of contact.

The slope of the tangent must be the same as the $\frac{dy}{dx}$ of the curve ; that is, $2x - 5$.

The equation of the straight line is $y = ax + b$, and as it is satisfied for the values $x = 2$, $y = -1$, then $-1 = a \times 2 + b$; also, its $\frac{dy}{dx} = a = 2x - 5$.

The x and the y of the point of contact must also satisfy both the equation of the tangent and the equation of the curve.

We have then

$$
\left\{
\begin{aligned}
y &= x^2 - 5x + 6, & \ldots\ldots\ldots\ldots\ldots\ldots &\text{(i)} \\
y &= ax + b, & \ldots\ldots\ldots\ldots\ldots\ldots\ldots &\text{(ii)} \\
-1 &= 2a + b, & \ldots\ldots\ldots\ldots\ldots\ldots\ldots &\text{(iii)} \\
a &= 2x - 5, & \ldots\ldots\ldots\ldots\ldots\ldots\ldots &\text{(iv)}
\end{aligned}
\right.
$$

four equations in a, b, x, y.

Equations (i) and (ii) give $x^2 - 5x + 6 = ax + b$.

Replacing a and b by their value in this, we get

$$x^2 - 5x + 6 = (2x - 5)x - 1 - 2(2x - 5),$$

which simplifies to $x^2 - 4x + 3 = 0$, the solutions of which are : $x = 3$ and $x = 1$. Replacing in (i), we get $y = 0$ and $y = 2$ respectively ; the two points of contact are then $x = 1$, $y = 2$; and $x = 3$, $y = 0$.

Note.—In all exercises dealing with curves, students will find it extremely instructive to verify the deductions obtained by actually plotting the curves.

EXERCISES VIII

(See page 243 for Answers)

(1) Plot the curve $y = \frac{3}{4}x^2 - 5$, using a scale of millimetres. Measure at points corresponding to different values of x, the angle of its slope.

Find, by differentiating the equation, the expression for slope ; and see, from a Table of Natural Tangents, whether this agrees with the measured angle.

(2) Find what will be the slope of the curve

$$y = 0 \cdot 12x^3 - 2,$$

at the particular point that has as abscissa $x = 2$.

(3) If $y = (x - a)(x - b)$, show that at the particular point of the curve where $\dfrac{dy}{dx} = 0$, x will have the value $\frac{1}{2}(a + b)$.

(4) Find the $\frac{dy}{dx}$ of the equation $y = x^3 + 3x$; and calculate the numerical values of $\frac{dy}{dx}$ for the points corresponding to $x = 0$, $x = \frac{1}{2}$, $x = 1$, $x = 2$.

(5) In the curve to which the equation is $x^2 + y^2 = 4$, find the values of x at those points where the slope $= 1$.

(6) Find the slope, at any point, of the curve whose equation is $\frac{x^2}{3^2} + \frac{y^2}{2^2} = 1$; and give the numerical value of the slope at the place where $x = 0$, and at that where $x = 1$.

(7) The equation of a tangent to the curve $y = 5 - 2x + 0.5x^3$, being of the form $y = mx + n$, where m and n are constants, find the value of m and n if the point where the tangent touches the curve has $x = 2$ for abscissa.

(8) At what angle do the two curves
$$y = 3.5x^2 + 2 \quad \text{and} \quad y = x^2 - 5x + 9.5$$
cut one another?

(9) Tangents to the curve $y = \pm\sqrt{25 - x^2}$ are drawn at points for which $x = 3$ and $x = 4$, the value of y being positive. Find the coordinates of the point of intersection of the tangents and their mutual inclination.

(10) A straight line $y = 2x - b$ touches a curve $y = 3x^2 + 2$ at one point. What are the coordinates of the point of contact. and what is the value of b?

CHAPTER XI

MAXIMA AND MINIMA

A QUANTITY which varies continuously is said to pass by (or through) a maximum or minimum value when, in the course of its variation, the immediately preceding and following values are *both* smaller or greater, respectively, than the value referred to. An infinitely great value is therefore not a maximum value.

One of the principal uses of the process of differentiating is to find out under what conditions the value of the thing differentiated becomes a maximum, or a minimum. This is often exceedingly important in engineering questions, where it is most desirable to know what conditions will make the cost of working a minimum, or will make the efficiency a maximum.

Now, to begin with a concrete case, let us take the equation

$$y = x^2 - 4x + 7.$$

By assigning a number of successive values to x, and finding the corresponding values of y, we can readily see that the equation represents a curve with a minimum.

x	0	1	2	3	4	5
y	7	4	3	4	7	12

These values are plotted in Fig. 26, which shows that y has apparently a minimum value of 3, when x is made equal to 2. But are you sure that the minimum occurs at 2, and not at $2\frac{1}{4}$ or at $1\frac{3}{4}$?

Of course it would be possible with any algebraic expression to work out a lot of values, and in this way arrive gradually at the particular value that may be a maximum or a minimum.

Here is another example :

Let $y = 3x - x^2.$

Calculate a few values thus :

x	-1	0	1	2	3	4	5
y	-4	0	2	2	0	-4	-10

Plot these values as in Fig. 27.

It will be evident that there will be a maximum somewhere

Fig. 26.

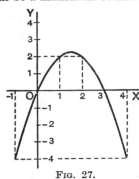

Fig. 27.

between $x = 1$ and $x = 2$; and the thing *looks* as if the maximum value of y ought to be about $2\frac{1}{4}$. Try some intermediate values. If $x = 1\frac{1}{4}$, $y = 2 \cdot 187$; if $x = 1\frac{1}{2}$, $y = 2 \cdot 25$; if $x = 1 \cdot 6$, $y = 2 \cdot 24$. How can we be sure that $2 \cdot 25$ is the real maximum, or that it occurs exactly when $x = 1\frac{1}{2}$?

Now it may sound like juggling to be assured that there is a way by which one can arrive straight at a maximum (or minimum) value without making a lot of preliminary trials or guesses. And that way depends on differentiating. Look back to pages 68–9 for the remarks about Figs. 14 and 15, and you will see that whenever a curve gets either to its maximum or to its minimum height, at that point its $\frac{dy}{dx} = 0.$

Now this gives us the clue to the dodge that is wanted. When there is put before you an equation, and you want to find that value of x that will make its y a minimum (or a maximum), *first differentiate it,* and having done so, write its $\frac{dy}{dx}$ as *equal to zero,* and then solve for x. Put this particular value of x into the original equation, and you will then get the required value of y. This process is commonly called " equating to zero ".

To see how simply it works, take the example with which this chapter opens, namely,

$$y = x^2 - 4x + 7.$$

Differentiating, we get :

$$\frac{dy}{dx} = 2x - 4.$$

Now equate this to zero, thus :

$$2x - 4 = 0.$$

Solving this equation for x, we get :

$$2x = 4, \quad x = 2.$$

Now, we know that the maximum (or minimum) will occur exactly when $x = 2$.

Putting the value $x = 2$ into the original equation, we get

$$y = 2^2 - (4 \times 2) + 7$$
$$= 4 - 8 + 7 = 3.$$

Now look back at Fig. 26, and you will see that the minimum occurs when $x = 2$, and that this minimum of $y = 3$.

Try the second example (Fig. 27), which is

$$y = 3x - x^2.$$

Differentiating, $\qquad \dfrac{dy}{dx} = 3 - 2x.$

Equating to zero, $\quad 3 - 2x = 0,$

whence $\qquad\qquad\qquad x = 1\tfrac{1}{2} \; ;$

and putting this value of x into the original equation, we find :

$$y = 4\tfrac{1}{2} - (1\tfrac{1}{2} \times 1\tfrac{1}{2}),$$
$$y = 2\tfrac{1}{4}.$$

This gives us exactly the information as to which the method of trying a lot of values left us uncertain.

Now, before we go on to any further cases, we have two remarks to make. When you are told to equate $\dfrac{dy}{dx}$ to zero, you feel at first (that is if you have any wits of your own) a kind of resentment, because you know that $\dfrac{dy}{dx}$ has all sorts of different values at different parts of the curve, according to whether it is sloping up or down. So, when you are suddenly told to write

$$\frac{dy}{dx} = 0,$$

you resent it, and feel inclined to say that it can't be true. Now you will have to understand the essential difference between " an equation ", and " an equation of condition ". Ordinarily you are dealing with equations that are true in themselves ; but, on occasions, of which the present are examples, you have to write down equations that are not necessarily true, but are only true if certain conditions are to be fulfilled ; and you write them down in order, by solving them, to find the conditions which make them true. Now we want to find the particular value that x has when the curve is neither sloping up nor sloping down, that is, at the particular place where $\dfrac{dy}{dx} = 0$. So, writing $\dfrac{dy}{dx} = 0$ does *not* mean that it always is $= 0$; but you write it down *as a condition* in order to see how much x will come out if $\dfrac{dy}{dx}$ is to be zero.

The second remark is one which (if you have any wits of

your own) you will probably have already made : namely, that this much-belauded process of equating to zero entirely fails to tell you whether the x that you thereby find is going to give you a *maximum* value of y or a *minimum* value of y. Quite so. It does not of itself discriminate ; it finds for you the right value of x but leaves you to find out for yourselves whether the corresponding y is a maximum or a minimum. Of course, if you have plotted the curve, you know already which it will be.

For instance, take the equation :

$$y = 4x + \frac{1}{x}.$$

Without stopping to think what curve it corresponds to, differentiate it, and equate to zero :

$$\frac{dy}{dx} = 4 - x^{-2} = 4 - \frac{1}{x^2} = 0 ;$$

whence $\qquad x = \frac{1}{2}$;

and, inserting this value,

$$y = 4$$

will be either a maximum or else a minimum. But which? You will hereafter be told a way, depending upon a second differentiation (see Chap. XII, p. 93). But at present it is enough if you will simply try any other value of x differing a little from the one found, and see whether with this altered value the corresponding value of y is less or greater than that already found.

Try another simple problem in maxima and minima. Suppose you were asked to divide any number into two parts, such that the product was a maximum? How would you set about it if you did not know the trick of equating to zero? I suppose you could worry it out by the rule of try, try, try again. Let 60 be the number. You can try cutting it into two parts, and multiplying them together. Thus, 50 times 10 is 500 ; 52 times 8 is 416 ; 40 times 20 is 800 ; 45 times 15 is 675 ; 30 times 30 is 900. This looks like a maximum : try varying it. 31 times 29 is 899, which is not so good ; and 32 times 28 is 896, which is worse. So it seems that the biggest product will be got by dividing into two halves.

Now see what the calculus tells you. Let the number to be cut into two parts be called n. Then if x is one part, the other will be $n - x$, and the product will be $x(n - x)$ or $nx - x^2$. So we write $y = nx - x^2$. Now differentiate and equate to zero ;

$$\frac{dy}{dx} = n - 2x = 0.$$

Solving for x, we get $\quad \frac{n}{2} = x.$

So now we *know* that whatever number n may be, we must divide it into two equal parts if the product of the parts is to be a maximum ; and the value of that maximum product will always be $= \frac{1}{4}n^2$.

This is a very useful rule, and applies to any number of factors, so that if $m + n + p =$ a constant number, $m \times n \times p$ is a maximum when $m = n = p$.

Test Case.

Let us at once apply our knowledge to a case that we can test.

Let $\qquad y = x^2 - x$;

and let us find whether this function has a maximum or minimum ; and if so, test whether it is a maximum or a minimum.

Differentiating, we get

$$\frac{dy}{dx} = 2x - 1.$$

Equating to zero, we get

$$2x - 1 = 0,$$
whence $\qquad 2x = 1,$
or $\qquad x = \frac{1}{2}.$

That is to say, when x is made $= \frac{1}{2}$, the corresponding value of y will be either a maximum or a minimum. Accordingly, putting $x = \frac{1}{2}$ in the original equation, we get

$$y = (\tfrac{1}{2})^2 - \tfrac{1}{2},$$
or $\qquad y = -\tfrac{1}{4}.$

Is this a maximum or a minimum? To test it, try putting x a little bigger than $\frac{1}{2}$—say, make $x = 0\cdot6$. Then

$$y = (0\cdot6)^2 - 0\cdot6 = 0\cdot36 - 0\cdot6 = -0\cdot24,$$

which is higher up than $-0\cdot25$; showing that $y = -0\cdot25$ is a *minimum*.

Plot the curve for yourself, and verify the calculation.

Further Examples.

A most interesting example is afforded by a curve that has both a maximum and a minimum. Its equation is :

$$y = \tfrac{1}{3}x^3 - 2x^2 + 3x + 1.$$
Now $\qquad \dfrac{dy}{dx} = x^2 - 4x + 3.$

Equating to zero, we get the quadratic,

$$x^2 - 4x + 3 = 0 ;$$

and solving the quadratic gives us *two* roots, viz.

$$\begin{cases} x = 3 \\ x = 1. \end{cases}$$

Now, when $x = 3$, $y = 1$; and when $x = 1$, $y = 2\frac{1}{3}$. The first of these is a minimum, the second a maximum.

The curve itself may be plotted (as in Fig. 28) from the values calculated, as below, from the original equation.

x	-1	0	1	2	3	4	5	6
y	$-4\frac{1}{3}$	1	$2\frac{1}{3}$	$1\frac{2}{3}$	1	$2\frac{1}{3}$	$7\frac{2}{3}$	19

A further exercise in maxima and minima is afforded by the following example :

The equation to a circle of radius r, having its centre C at the point whose coordinates are $x = a$, $y = b$, as depicted in Fig. 29, is :

$$(y - b)^2 + (x - a)^2 = r^2.$$

FIG. 28.

FIG. 29.

This may be transformed into

$$y = \sqrt{r^2 - (x - a)^2} + b.$$

Now we know beforehand, by mere inspection of the figure, that when $x = a$, y will be either at its maximum value, $b + r$, or else at its minimum value, $b - r$. But let us not take advantage of this knowledge ; let us set about finding what value of x will make y a maximum or a minimum, by the process of differentiating and equating to zero.

$$\frac{dy}{dx} = \frac{1}{2} \frac{1}{\sqrt{r^2 - (x-a)^2}} \times (2a - 2x),$$

which reduces to

$$\frac{dy}{dx} = \frac{a - x}{\sqrt{r^2 - (x-a)^2}}.$$

Then the condition for y being maximum or minimum is :

$$\frac{a - x}{\sqrt{r^2 - (x-a)^2}} = 0.$$

Since no value whatever of x will make the denominator infinite, the only condition to give zero is

$$x = a.$$

Inserting this value in the original equation for the circle, we find

$$y = \sqrt{r^2} + b \ ;$$

and as the root of r^2 is either $+r$ or $-r$, we have two resulting values of y,

$$\begin{cases} y = b + r, \\ y = b - r. \end{cases}$$

The first of these is the maximum, at the top ; the second the minimum, at the bottom.

If the curve is such that there is no place that is a maximum or minimum, the process of equating to zero will yield an impossible result. For instance :

Let $\qquad\qquad y = ax^3 + bx + c.$

Then $\qquad\qquad \dfrac{dy}{dx} = 3ax^2 + b.$

Equating this to zero, we get $3ax^2 + b = 0$, $x^2 = \dfrac{-b}{3a}$, and $x = \sqrt{\dfrac{-b}{3a}}$, which is impossible, supposing a and b to have the same sign.

Therefore y has no maximum nor minimum.

A few more worked examples will enable you to thoroughly master this most interesting and useful application of the calculus.

(1) What are the sides of the rectangle of maximum area inscribed in a circle of radius R?

If one side be called x,

$$\text{the other side} = \sqrt{(\text{diagonal})^2 - x^2} \; ;$$

and as the diagonal of the rectangle is necessarily a diameter of the circumscribing circle, the other side $= \sqrt{4R^2 - x^2}$.

Then, area of rectangle $S = x\sqrt{4R^2 - x^2}$,

$$\frac{dS}{dx} = x \times \frac{d(\sqrt{4R^2 - x^2})}{dx} + \sqrt{4R^2 - x^2} \times \frac{d(x)}{dx}.$$

If you have forgotten how to differentiate $\sqrt{4R^2 - x^2}$, here is a hint : write $w = 4R^2 - x^2$ and $y = \sqrt{w}$, and seek $\frac{dy}{dw}$ and $\frac{dw}{dx}$; fight it out, and only if you can't get on refer to page 57.

You will get

$$\frac{dS}{dx} = x \times -\frac{x}{\sqrt{4R^2 - x^2}} + \sqrt{4R^2 - x^2} = \frac{4R^2 - 2x^2}{\sqrt{4R^2 - x^2}}.$$

For maximum or minimum we must have

$$\frac{4R^2 - 2x^2}{\sqrt{4R^2 - x^2}} = 0 \; ;$$

that is, $4R^2 - 2x^2 = 0$ and $x = R\sqrt{2}$.

The other side $= \sqrt{4R^2 - 2R^2} = R\sqrt{2}$; the two sides are equal ; the figure is a square the side of which is equal to the diagonal of the square constructed on the radius. In this case it is, of course, a maximum with which we are dealing.

(2) What is the radius of the opening of a conical vessel the sloping side of which has a length l when the capacity of the vessel is greatest?

If R be the radius and H the corresponding height,

$$H = \sqrt{l^2 - R^2}.$$

Volume $\quad V = \pi R^2 \times \dfrac{H}{3} = \pi R^2 \times \dfrac{\sqrt{l^2 - R^2}}{3}.$

Proceeding as in the previous problem, we get

$$\frac{dV}{dR} = \pi R^2 \times -\frac{R}{3\sqrt{l^2 - R^2}} + \frac{2\pi R}{3}\sqrt{l^2 - R^2}$$

$$= \frac{2\pi R(l^2 - R^2) - \pi R^3}{3\sqrt{l^2 - R^2}} = 0$$

for maximum or minimum.

Or, $2\pi R(l^2 - R^2) - \pi R^3 = 0$, and $R = l\sqrt{\tfrac{2}{3}}$, for a maximum, obviously.

(3) Find the maxima and minima of the function

$$y = \frac{x}{4-x} + \frac{4-x}{x}.$$

We get $\quad \dfrac{dy}{dx} = \dfrac{(4-x)-(-x)}{(4-x)^2} + \dfrac{-x-(4-x)}{x^2} = 0$

for maximum or minimum ; or

$$\frac{4}{(4-x)^2} - \frac{4}{x^2} = 0 \quad \text{and} \quad x = 2.$$

There is only one value, hence only one maximum or minimum.

$$\begin{array}{lll} \text{For} & x = 2, & y = 2, \\ \text{for} & x = 1{\cdot}5, & y = 2{\cdot}27, \\ \text{for} & x = 2{\cdot}5, & y = 2{\cdot}27 \; ; \end{array}$$

it is therefore a minimum. (It is instructive to plot the graph of the function.)

(4) Find the maxima and minima of the function

$$y = \sqrt{1+x} + \sqrt{1-x}.$$

(It will be found instructive to plot the graph.)

Differentiating gives at once (see example No. 1, p. 58)

$$\frac{dy}{dx} = \frac{1}{2\sqrt{1+x}} - \frac{1}{2\sqrt{1-x}} = 0$$

for maximum or minimum.

Hence $\sqrt{1+x} = \sqrt{1-x}$ and $x = 0$, the only solution

For $x = 0$, $\quad y = 2$.

For $x = \pm 0 \cdot 5$, $y = 1 \cdot 932$, so this is a maximum.

(5) Find the maxima and minima of the function

$$y = \frac{x^2 - 5}{2x - 4}.$$

We have $\qquad \dfrac{dy}{dx} = \dfrac{(2x - 4) \times 2x - (x^2 - 5)2}{(2x - 4)^2} = 0$

for maximum or minimum ; or

$$\frac{2x^2 - 8x + 10}{(2x - 4)^2} = 0 \ ;$$

or $x^2 - 4x + 5 = 0$; which has solutions

$$x = 2 \pm \sqrt{-1}.$$

These being imaginary, there is no real value of x for which $\dfrac{dy}{dx} = 0$; hence there is neither maximum nor minimum.

(6) Find the maxima and minima of the function

$$(y - x^2)^2 = x^5.$$

This may be written $y = x^2 \pm x^{\frac{5}{2}}$.

$$\frac{dy}{dx} = 2x \pm \tfrac{5}{2} x^{\frac{3}{2}} = 0 \text{ for maximum or minimum } ;$$

that is, $x(2 \pm \tfrac{5}{2} x^{\frac{1}{2}}) = 0$, which is satisfied for $x = 0$, and for $2 \pm \tfrac{5}{2} x^{\frac{1}{2}} = 0$, that is for $x = \tfrac{16}{25}$. So there are two solutions.

Taking first $x=0$. If $x=-0.5$, $y=0.25 \pm \sqrt[2]{-(.5)^5}$, and if $x=+0.5$, $y=0.25 \pm \sqrt[2]{(.5)^5}$. On one side y is imaginary ; that

is, there is no value of y that can be represented by a graph ; the latter is therefore entirely on the right side of the axis of y (see Fig. 30).

On plotting the graph it will be found that the curve goes to the origin, as if there were a minimum there ; but instead of continuing beyond, as it should do for a minimum, it retraces its steps (forming what is called a

FIG. 30.

" cusp "). There is no minimum, therefore, although the condition for a minimum is satisfied, namely $\dfrac{dy}{dx}=0$. It is necessary therefore always to check by taking one value on either side.

Now, if we take $x=\frac{16}{25}=0.64$. If $x=0.64$, $y=0.7373$ and $y=0.0819$; if $x=0.6$, y becomes 0.6389 and 0.0811 ; and if $x=0.7$, y becomes 0.8996 and 0.0804.

This shows that there are two branches of the curve ; the upper one does not pass through a maximum, but the lower one does.

(7) A cylinder whose height is twice the radius of the base is increasing in volume, so that all its parts keep always in the same proportion to each other ; that is, at any instant, the cylinder is *similar* to the original cylinder. When the radius of the base is r feet, the surface area is increasing at the rate of 20 square inches per second ; at what rate per second is its volume then increasing?

$$\text{Area} = S = 2(\pi r^2) + 2\pi r \times 2r = 6\pi r^2.$$

$$\text{Volume} = V = \pi r^2 \times 2r = 2\pi r^3.$$

$$\frac{dS}{dt} = 12\pi r \frac{dr}{dt} = 20 \; ; \quad \frac{dr}{dt} = \frac{20}{12\pi r} \; ;$$

$$\frac{dV}{dt} = 6\pi r^2 \frac{dr}{dt} \; ; \quad \text{and}$$

$$\frac{dV}{dt} = 6\pi r^2 \times \frac{20}{12\pi r} = 10r.$$

The volume changes at the rate of $10r$ cubic inches per second.

Make other examples for yourself. There are few subjects which offer such a wealth for interesting examples.

EXERCISES IX

(See page 243 for Answers)

(1) What values of x will make y a maximum and a minimum, if $y = \dfrac{x^2}{x+1}$?

(2) What value of x will make y a maximum in the equation $y = \dfrac{x}{a^2 + x^2}$?

(3) A line of length p is to be cut up into 4 parts and put together as a rectangle. Show that the area of the rectangle will be a maximum if each of its sides is equal to $\frac{1}{4}p$.

(4) A piece of string 30 inches long has its two ends joined together and is stretched by 3 pegs so as to form a triangle. What is the largest triangular area that can be enclosed by the string?

(Hint : Apply rule on p. 83, ten lines from foot.)

D

(5) Plot the curve corresponding to the equation

$$y = \frac{10}{x} + \frac{10}{8-x} \; ;$$

also find $\frac{dy}{dx}$, and deduce the value of x that will make y a minimum ; and find that minimum value of y.

(6) If $y = x^5 - 5x$, find what values of x will make y a maximum or a minimum.

(7) What is the smallest square that can be inscribed in a given square?

(8) Inscribe in a given cone, the height of which is equal to the radius of the base, a cylinder (a) whose volume is a maximum ; (b) whose lateral area is a maximum ; (c) whose total area is a maximum.

(9) Inscribe in a sphere, a cylinder (a) whose volume is a maximum ; (b) whose lateral area is a maximum ; (c) whose total area is a maximum.

(10) A spherical balloon is increasing in volume. If, when its radius is r feet, its volume is increasing at the rate of 4 cubic feet per second, at what rate is its surface then increasing?

(11) Inscribe in a given sphere a cone whose volume is a maximum.

(12) The current C given by a battery of N similar voltaic cells is $C = \dfrac{n \times E}{R + \dfrac{rn^2}{N}}$, where E, R, r, are constants and n is the number of cells coupled in series. Find the relation between n and N for which the current is greatest.

CHAPTER XII

CURVATURE OF CURVES

RETURNING to the process of successive differentiation, it may be asked : Why does anybody want to differentiate twice over? We know that when the variable quantities are space and time, by differentiating twice over we get the acceleration of a moving body, and that in the geometrical interpretation, as applied to curves, $\dfrac{dy}{dx}$ means the *slope* of the curve. But what can $\dfrac{d^2y}{dx^2}$ mean in this case? Clearly it means the rate (per unit of length x) at which the slope is changing—in brief,

FIG. 31.

FIG. 32.

it is *an indication of the manner in which the slope of the portion of curve considered varies*, that is, whether the slope of the curve increases or decreases when x increases, or, in other words, whether the curve curves up or down towards the right.

Suppose a slope constant, as in Fig. 31.

Here, $\dfrac{dy}{dx}$ is of constant value.

Suppose, however, a case in which, like Fig. 32, the slope

Fig. 33.

itself is getting greater upwards ; then

$$\frac{d\left(\dfrac{dy}{dx}\right)}{dx},$$ that is, $\frac{d^2y}{dx^2}$, will be *positive*.

If the slope is becoming less as you go to the right (as in Fig. 14, p. 68), or as in Fig. 33, then, even though the curve may be going upward, since the change is such as to diminish

its slope, its $\frac{d^2y}{dx^2}$ will be *negative*.

It is now time to initiate you into another secret—how to tell whether the result that you get by " equating to zero " is a maximum or a minimum. The trick is this : After you have differentiated (so as to get the expression which you equate to zero), you then differentiate a second time and look whether the result of the second differentiation is *positive* or *negative*. If $\frac{d^2y}{dx^2}$ comes out *positive*, then you know that the value of y which you got was a *minimum* ; but if $\frac{d^2y}{dx^2}$ comes out *negative*, then the value of y which you got must be a *maximum*. That's the rule.

The reason of it ought to be quite evident. Think of any curve that has a minimum point in it, like Fig. 15 (p. 68), or like Fig. 34, where the point of minimum y is marked M, and the curve is *concave* upwards. To the left of M the slope is downward, that is, negative, and is getting less negative. To the right of M the slope has become upward, and is getting more and more upward.

Fig. 34.

Clearly the change of slope as the curve passes through M is such that $\dfrac{d^2y}{dx^2}$ is *positive*, for its operation, as x increases toward the right, is to convert a downward slope into an upward one.

Similarly, consider any curve that has a maximum point in it, like Fig. 16 (p. 69), or like Fig. 35, where the curve is *convex*, and the maximum point is marked M. In this case, as the curve passes through M from left to right, its upward slope is converted into a downward or negative slope, so that in this case the " slope of the slope " $\dfrac{d^2y}{dx^2}$ is *negative*.

FIG. 35.

Go back now to the examples of the last chapter and verify in this way the conclusions arrived at as to whether in any particular case there is a maximum or a minimum. You will find below a few worked-out examples.

────────

(1) Find the maximum or minimum of

$$(a)\ \ y = 4x^2 - 9x - 6 \ ; \quad (b)\ \ y = 6 + 9x - 4x^2 \ ;$$

and ascertain if it be a maximum or a minimum in each case.

$(a)\ \dfrac{dy}{dx} = 8x - 9 = 0 \ ; \ \ x = 1\tfrac{1}{8} \ ; \ \text{and}\ y = -11 \cdot 065.$

$\dfrac{d^2y}{dx^2} = 8 \ ; \ \text{it is} + \ ; \ \text{hence it is a minimum.}$

$(b)\ \dfrac{dy}{dx} = 9 - 8x = 0 \ ; \ \ x = 1\tfrac{1}{8} \ ; \ \text{and}\ y = +11 \cdot 065.$

$\dfrac{d^2y}{dx^2} = -8 \ ; \ \text{it is} - \ ; \ \text{hence it is a maximum.}$

(2) Find the maxima and minima of the function

$$y = x^3 - 3x + 16.$$

$$\frac{dy}{dx} = 3x^2 - 3 = 0 \; ; \quad x^2 = 1 \; ; \quad \text{and} \; x = \pm 1.$$

$$\frac{d^2y}{dx^2} = 6x \; ; \quad \text{for} \; x = 1 \; ; \quad \text{it is} \; + \; ;$$

hence $x = 1$ corresponds to a minimum $y = 14$. For $x = -1$ it is $-$; hence $x = -1$ corresponds to a maximum $y = +18$.

(3) Find the maxima and minima of $y = \dfrac{x-1}{x^2+2}$.

$$\frac{dy}{dx} = \frac{(x^2+2) \times 1 - (x-1) \times 2x}{(x^2+2)^2} = \frac{2x - x^2 + 2}{(x^2+2)^2} = 0 \; ;$$

or $x^2 - 2x - 2 = 0$, whose solutions are $x = +2 \cdot 73$ and $x = -0 \cdot 73$.

$$\frac{d^2y}{dx^2} = -\frac{(x^2+2)^2 \times (2x-2) - (x^2-2x-2)(4x^3+8x)}{(x^2+2)^4}$$

$$= \frac{2x^5 - 6x^4 - 8x^3 - 8x^2 - 24x + 8}{(x^2+2)^4}.$$

The denominator is always positive, so it is sufficient to ascertain the sign of the numerator.

If we put $x = 2 \cdot 73$, the numerator is negative ; the maximum, $y = 0 \cdot 183$.

If we put $x = -0 \cdot 73$, the numerator is positive ; the minimum, $y = -0 \cdot 683$.

(4) The expense C of handling the products of a certain factory varies with the weekly output P according to the relation $C = aP + \dfrac{b}{c+P} + d$, where a, b, c, d are positive constants. For what output will the expense be least?

$$\frac{dC}{dP} = a - \frac{b}{(c+P)^2} = 0 \quad \text{for maximum or minimum ; hence}$$

$$a = \frac{b}{(c+P)^2} \quad \text{and} \quad P = \pm\sqrt{\frac{b}{a}} - c.$$

As the output cannot be negative, $P = +\sqrt{\dfrac{b}{a}} - c.$

Now
$$\frac{d^2C}{dP^2} = + \frac{b(2c+2P)}{(c+P)^4},$$

which is positive for all the values of P; hence $P = +\sqrt{\dfrac{b}{a}} - c$ corresponds to a minimum.

(5) The total cost per hour C of lighting a building with N lamps of a certain kind is
$$C = N\left(\frac{C_l}{t} + \frac{EPC_e}{1000}\right),$$

where E is the commercial efficiency (watts per candle),

P is the candle power of each lamp,

t is the average life of each lamp in hours,

$C_l =$ cost of renewal in pence per hour of use,

$C_e =$ cost of energy per 1000 watts per hour.

Moreover, the relation connecting the average life of a lamp with the commercial efficiency at which it is run is approximately $t = mE^n$, where m and n are constants depending on the kind of lamp.

Find the commercial efficiency for which the total cost of lighting will be least.

We have
$$C = N\left(\frac{C_l}{m}E^{-n} + \frac{PC_e}{1000}E\right),$$
$$\frac{dC}{dE} = N\left(\frac{PC_e}{1000} - \frac{nC_l}{m}E^{-(n+1)}\right) = 0$$

for maximum or minimum.
$$E^{n+1} = \frac{1000 \times nC_l}{mPC_e} \quad \text{and} \quad E = \sqrt[n+1]{\frac{1000 \times nC_l}{mPC_e}}.$$

This is clearly for minimum, since
$$\frac{d^2C}{dE^2} = N\left[(n+1)\frac{nC_l}{m}E^{-(n+2)}\right],$$

which is positive for a positive value of E.

For a particular type of 16 candle-power lamps, $C_l = 17$ pence, $C_e = 5$ pence ; and it was found that $m = 10$ and $n = 3.6$.

$$E = \sqrt[4.6]{\frac{1000 \times 3.6 \times 17}{10 \times 16 \times 5}} = 2.6 \text{ watts per candle power.}$$

EXERCISES X

(*See page 243 for Answers*)

You are advised to plot the graph of any numerical example.

(1) Find the maxima and minima of

$$y = x^3 + x^2 - 10x + 8.$$

(2) Given $y = \dfrac{b}{a} x - cx^2$, find expressions for $\dfrac{dy}{dx}$, and for $\dfrac{d^2y}{dx^2}$; also find the value of x which makes y a maximum or a minimum, and show whether it is maximum or minimum.

(3) Find how many maxima and how many minima there are in the curve, the equation to which is

$$y = 1 - \frac{x^2}{2} + \frac{x^4}{24} ;$$

and how many in that of which the equation is

$$y = 1 - \frac{x^2}{2} + \frac{x^4}{24} - \frac{x^6}{720}.$$

(4) Find the maxima and minima of

$$y = 2x + 1 + \frac{5}{x^2}.$$

(5) Find the maxima and minima of

$$y = \frac{3}{x^2 + x + 1}.$$

(6) Find the maxima and minima of

$$y = \frac{5x}{2 + x^2}.$$

(7) Find the maxima and minima of

$$y = \frac{3x}{x^2 - 3} + \frac{x}{2} + 5.$$

(8) Divide a number N into two parts in such a way that three times the square of one part plus twice the square of the other part shall be a minimum.

(9) The efficiency u of an electric generator at different values of output x is expressed by the general equation :

$$u = \frac{x}{a + bx + cx^2} ;$$

where a is a constant depending chiefly on the energy losses in the iron and c a constant depending chiefly on the resistance of the copper parts. Find an expression for that value of the output at which the efficiency will be a maximum.

(10) Suppose it to be known that consumption of coal by a certain steamer may be represented by the formula

$$y = 0\cdot3 + 0\cdot001v^3 ;$$

where y is the number of tons of coal burned per hour and v is the speed expressed in nautical miles per hour. The cost of wages, interest on capital, and depreciation of that ship are together equal, per hour, to the cost of 1 ton of coal. What speed will make the total cost of a voyage of 1000 nautical miles a minimum? And, if coal costs 10 shillings per ton, what will that minimum cost of the voyage amount to?

(11) Find the maxima and minima of

$$y = \pm\frac{x}{6}\sqrt{x(10-x)}.$$

(12) Find the maxima and minima of

$$y = 4x^3 - x^2 - 2x + 1.$$

CHAPTER XIII

OTHER USEFUL DODGES

Partial Fractions

WE have seen that when we differentiate a fraction we have
to perform a rather complicated operation ; and, if the
fraction is not itself a simple one, the result is bound to be a
complicated expression. If we could split the fraction into
two or more simpler fractions such that their sum is equivalent to the original fraction, we could then proceed by
differentiating each of these simpler expressions. And the
result of differentiating would be the sum of two (or more)
differentials, each one of which is relatively simple ; while the
final expression, though of course it will be the same as that
which could be obtained without resorting to this dodge, is thus
obtained with much less effort and appears in a simplified form.

Let us see how to reach this result. Try first the job of
adding two fractions together to form a resultant fraction.
Take, for example, the two fractions $\frac{1}{x+1}$ and $\frac{2}{x-1}$. Every
schoolboy can add these together and find their sum to be
$\frac{3x+1}{x^2-1}$. And in the same way he can add together three or
more fractions. Now this process can certainly be reversed :
that is to say that, if this last expression were given, it is
certain that it can somehow be split back again into its
original components or partial fractions. Only we do not
know in every case that may be presented to us *how* we can
so split it. In order to find this out we shall consider a simple
case at first. But it is important to bear in mind that all
which follows applies only to what are called " proper "

algeoraic fractions, meaning fractions like the above, which have the numerator of *a lesser degree* than the denominator ; that is, those in which the highest index of x is less in the numerator than in the denominator. If we have to deal with such an expression as $\dfrac{x^2 + 2}{x^2 - 1}$, we can simplify it by division, since it is equivalent to $1 + \dfrac{3}{x^2 - 1}$; and $\dfrac{3}{x^2 - 1}$ is a proper algebraic fraction to which the operation of splitting into partial fractions can be applied, as explained hereafter.

Case I. If we perform many additions of two or more fractions the denominators of which contain only terms in x, and no terms in x^2, x^3, or any other powers of x, we *always* find that *the denominator of the final resulting fraction is the product of the denominators* of the fractions which were added to form the result. It follows that by factorizing the denominator of this final fraction, we can find every one of the denominators of the partial fractions of which we are in search.

Suppose we wish to go back from $\dfrac{3x + 1}{x^2 - 1}$ to the components which we know are $\dfrac{1}{x + 1}$ and $\dfrac{2}{x - 1}$. If we did not know what those components were we can still prepare the way by writing :

$$\frac{3x + 1}{x^2 - 1} = \frac{3x + 1}{(x + 1)(x - 1)} = \frac{}{x + 1} + \frac{}{x - 1},$$

leaving blank the places for the numerators until we know what to put there. We always may assume the sign between the partial fractions to be *plus*, since, if it be *minus*, we shall simply find the corresponding numerator to be negative. Now, since the partial fractions are *proper* fractions, the numerators are mere numbers without x at all, and we can call them A, B, C ... as we please. So, in this case, we have :

$$\frac{3x + 1}{x^2 - 1} = \frac{A}{x + 1} + \frac{B}{x - 1}.$$

If, now, we perform the addition of these two partial fractions, we get $\dfrac{A(x-1)+B(x+1)}{(x+1)(x-1)}$; and this must be equal to $\dfrac{3x+1}{(x+1)(x-1)}$. And, as the denominators in these two expressions are the same, the numerators must be equal, giving us :

$$3x+1 = A(x-1)+B(x+1).$$

Now, this is an equation with two unknown quantities, and it would seem that we need another equation before we can solve them and find A and B. But there is another way out of this difficulty. The equation must be true for all values of x ; therefore it must be true for such values of x as will cause $x-1$ and $x+1$ to become zero, that is for $x=1$ and for $x=-1$ respectively. If we make $x=1$, we get $4=(A\times 0)+(B\times 2)$, so that $B=2$; and if we make $x=-1$, we get

$$-2 = (A \times -2) + (B \times 0),$$

so that $A=1$. Replacing the A and B of the partial fractions by these new values, we find them to become $\dfrac{1}{x+1}$ and $\dfrac{2}{x-1}$; and the thing is done.

As a further example, let us take the fraction

$$\frac{4x^2+2x-14}{x^3+3x^2-x-3}.$$

The denominator becomes zero when x is given the value 1 ; hence $x-1$ is a factor of it, and obviously then the other factor will be x^2+4x+3 ; and this can again be decomposed into $(x+1)(x+3)$. So we may write the fraction thus :

$$\frac{4x^2+2x-14}{x^3+3x^2-x-3} = \frac{A}{x+1}+\frac{B}{x-1}+\frac{C}{x+3},$$

making three partial factors.

Proceeding as before, we find

$$4x^2+2x-14 = A(x-1)(x+3)+B(x+1)(x+3) \\ +C(x+1)(x-1).$$

Now, if we make $x = 1$, we get :

$$-8 = (A \times 0) + B(2 \times 4) + (C \times 0) ; \text{ that is, } B = -1.$$

If $x = -1$, we get

$$-12 = A(-2 \times 2) + (B \times 0) + (C \times 0) ; \text{ whence } A = 3.$$

If $x = -3$, we get :

$$16 = (A \times 0) + (B \times 0) + C(-2 \times -4) ; \text{ whence } C = 2.$$

So then the partial fractions are :

$$\frac{3}{x+1} - \frac{1}{x-1} + \frac{2}{x+3},$$

which is far easier to differentiate with respect to x than the complicated expression from which it is derived.

Case II. If some of the factors of the denominator contain terms in x^2, and are not conveniently put into factors, then the corresponding numerator may contain a term in x, as well as a simple number, and hence it becomes necessary to represent this unknown numerator not by the symbol A but by $Ax + B$; the rest of the calculation being made as before.

Try, for instance : $\dfrac{-x^2 - 3}{(x^2 + 1)(x + 1)}$.

$$\frac{-x^2 - 3}{(x^2 + 1)(x + 1)} = \frac{Ax + B}{x^2 + 1} + \frac{C}{x + 1} ;$$
$$-x^2 - 3 = (Ax + B)(x + 1) + C(x^2 + 1).$$

Putting $x = -1$, we get $-4 = C \times 2$; and $C = -2$;

hence $\qquad -x^2 - 3 = (Ax + B)(x + 1) - 2x^2 - 2$;

and $\qquad x^2 - 1 = Ax(x + 1) + B(x + 1).$

Putting $x = 0$, we get $-1 = B$;

hence $\quad x^2 - 1 = Ax(x + 1) - x - 1$; or $x^2 + x = Ax(x + 1)$;

and $\qquad\qquad x + 1 = A(x + 1),$

so that $A = 1$, and the partial fractions are :

$$\frac{x - 1}{x^2 + 1} - \frac{2}{x + 1}.$$

Take as another example the fraction

$$\frac{x^3-2}{(x^2+1)(x^2+2)}.$$

We get $\dfrac{x^3-2}{(x^2+1)(x^2+2)} = \dfrac{Ax+B}{x^2+1} + \dfrac{Cx+D}{x^2+2}$

$$= \frac{(Ax+B)(x^2+2)+(Cx+D)(x^2+1)}{(x^2+1)(x^2+2)}.$$

In this case the determination of A, B, C, D is not so easy. It will be simpler to proceed as follows : Since the given fraction and the fraction found by adding the partial fractions are equal, and have *identical* denominators, the numerators must also be identically the same. In such a case, and for such algebraical expressions as those with which we are dealing here, *the coefficients of the same powers of x are equal and of same sign.*

Hence, since

$$x^3-2 = (Ax+B)(x^2+2)+(Cx+D)(x^2+1)$$
$$= (A+C)x^3 + (B+D)x^2 + (2A+C)x + 2B+D,$$

we have $1 = A+C$; $0 = B+D$ (the coefficient of x^2 in the left expression being zero) ; $0 = 2A+C$; and $-2 = 2B+D$. Here are four equations, from which we readily obtain $A = -1$; $B = -2$; $C = 2$; $D = 2$; so that the partial fractions are $\dfrac{2(x+1)}{x^2+2} - \dfrac{x+2}{x^2+1}$. This method can always be used ; but the method shown first will be found the quickest in the case of factors in x only.

Case III. When among the factors of the denominator there are some which are raised to some power, one must allow for the possible existence of partial fractions having for denominator the several powers of that factor up to the highest. For instance, in splitting the fraction $\dfrac{3x^2-2x+1}{(x+1)^2(x-2)}$

we must allow for the possible existence of a denominator $x+1$ as well as $(x+1)^2$ and $(x-2)$.

It may be thought, however, that, since the numerator of the fraction the denominator of which is $(x+1)^2$ may contain terms in x, we must allow for this in writing $Ax+B$ for its numerator, so that

$$\frac{3x^2-2x+1}{(x+1)^2(x-2)} = \frac{Ax+B}{(x+1)^2} + \frac{C}{x+1} + \frac{D}{x-2}.$$

If, however, we try to find A, B, C and D in this case, we fail, because we get four unknowns; and we have only three relations connecting them, yet

$$\frac{3x^2-2x+1}{(x+1)^2(x-2)} = \frac{x-1}{(x+1)^2} + \frac{1}{x+1} + \frac{1}{x-2}.$$

But if we write

$$\frac{3x^2-2x+1}{(x+1)^2(x-2)} = \frac{A}{(x+1)^2} + \frac{B}{x+1} + \frac{C}{x-2},$$

we get $\quad 3x^2-2x+1 = A(x-2) + B(x+1)(x-2) + C(x+1)^2.$

For $\quad x=-1$; $\quad 6=-3A$, or $A=-2$.

For $\quad x=2$; $\quad 9=9C$, or $C=1$.

For $\quad x=0$; $\quad 1=-2A-2B+C$.

Putting in the values of A and C:

$$1=4-2B+1, \text{ from which } B=2.$$

Hence the partial fractions are:

$$\frac{2}{x+1} - \frac{2}{(x+1)^2} + \frac{1}{x-2},$$

instead of $\dfrac{1}{x+1} + \dfrac{x-1}{(x+1)^2} + \dfrac{1}{x-2}$ stated above as being the

fractions from which $\dfrac{3x^2-2x+1}{(x+1)^2(x-2)}$ was obtained. The

mystery is cleared if we observe that $\dfrac{x-1}{(x+1)^2}$ can itself be split into the two fractions $\dfrac{1}{x+1} - \dfrac{2}{(x+1)^2}$, so that the three fractions given are really equivalent to

$$\frac{1}{x+1} + \frac{1}{x+1} - \frac{2}{(x+1)^2} + \frac{1}{x-2} = \frac{2}{x+1} - \frac{2}{(x+1)^2} + \frac{1}{x-2},$$

which are the partial fractions obtained.

We see that it is sufficient to allow for one numerical term in each numerator, and that we always get the ultimate partial fractions.

When there is a power of a factor of x^2 in the denominator, however, the corresponding numerators must be of the form $Ax + B$; for example,

$$\frac{3x-1}{(2x^2-1)^2(x+1)} = \frac{Ax+B}{(2x^2-1)^2} + \frac{Cx+D}{2x^2-1} + \frac{E}{x+1},$$

which gives

$$3x - 1 = (Ax+B)(x+1) + (Cx+D)(x+1)(2x^2-1) + E(2x^2-1)^2.$$

For $x = -1$, this gives $E = -4$. Replacing, transposing, collecting like terms, and dividing by $x+1$, we get

$$16x^3 - 16x^2 + 3 = 2Cx^3 + 2Dx^2 + x(A-C) + (B-D).$$

Hence $2C = 16$ and $C = 8$; $2D = -16$ and $D = -8$; $A - C = 0$ or $A - 8 = 0$ and $A = 8$; and finally, $B - D = 3$ or $B = -5$. So that we obtain as the partial fractions :

$$\frac{8x-5}{(2x^2-1)^2} + \frac{8(x-1)}{2x^2-1} - \frac{4}{x+1}.$$

It is useful to check the results obtained. The simplest way is to replace x by a single value, say $+1$, both in the given expression and in the partial fractions obtained.

Whenever the denominator contains but a power of a single factor, a very quick method is as follows :

Taking, for example, $\dfrac{4x+1}{(x+1)^3}$, let $x+1 = z$; then $x = z - 1$.

Replacing, we get

$$\frac{4(z-1)+1}{z^3} = \frac{4z-3}{z^3} = \frac{4}{z^2} - \frac{3}{z^3}.$$

The partial fractions are, therefore,

$$\frac{4}{(x+1)^2} - \frac{3}{(x+1)^3}.$$

Applying this to differentiation, let it be required to differentiate $y = \dfrac{5-4x}{6x^2+7x-3}$; we have

$$\frac{dy}{dx} = -\frac{(6x^2+7x-3) \times 4 + (5-4x)(12x+7)}{(6x^2+7x-3)^2}$$

$$= \frac{24x^2 - 60x - 23}{(6x^2+7x-3)^2}.$$

If we split the given expression into

$$\frac{1}{3x-1} - \frac{2}{2x+3}$$

we get, however,

$$\frac{dy}{dx} = -\frac{3}{(3x-1)^2} + \frac{4}{(2x+3)^2},$$

which is really the same result as above split into partial fractions. But the splitting, if done after differentiating, is more complicated, as will easily be seen. When we shall deal with the *integration* of such expressions, we shall find the splitting into partial fractions a precious auxiliary (see p. 192).

EXERCISES XI

(See page 244 for Answers)

Split into partial fractions :

(1) $\dfrac{3x+5}{(x-3)(x+4)}$.

(2) $\dfrac{3x-4}{(x-1)(x-2)}$.

(3) $\dfrac{3x+5}{x^2+x-12}$.

(4) $\dfrac{x+1}{x^2-7x+12}$.

(5) $\dfrac{x-8}{(2x+3)(3x-2)}$.

(6) $\dfrac{x^2-13x+26}{(x-2)(x-3)(x-4)}$.

(7) $\dfrac{x^2-3x+1}{(x-1)(x+2)(x-3)}$.

(8) $\dfrac{5x^2+7x+1}{(2x+1)(3x-2)(3x+1)}$.

(9) $\dfrac{x^2}{x^3-1}$.

(10) $\dfrac{x^4+1}{x^3+1}$.

(11) $\dfrac{5x^2+6x+4}{(x+1)(x^2+x+1)}$.

(12) $\dfrac{x}{(x-1)(x-2)^2}$.

(13) $\dfrac{x}{(x^2-1)(x+1)}$.

(14) $\dfrac{x+3}{(x+2)^2(x-1)}$.

(15) $\dfrac{3x^2+2x+1}{(x+2)(x^2+x+1)^2}$.

(16) $\dfrac{5x^2+8x-12}{(x+4)^3}$.

(17) $\dfrac{7x^2+9x-1}{(3x-2)^4}$.

(18) $\dfrac{x^2}{(x^3-8)(x-2)}$.

Differential of an Inverse Function

Consider the function (see p. 11) $y=3x$; it can be expressed in the form $x=\dfrac{y}{3}$; this latter form is called the *inverse function* to the one originally given.

If $y=3x$, $\dfrac{dy}{dx}=3$; if $x=\dfrac{y}{3}$, $\dfrac{dx}{dy}=\dfrac{1}{3}$, and we see that

$$\frac{dy}{dx}=\frac{1}{\dfrac{dx}{dy}} \quad \text{or} \quad \frac{dy}{dx}\times\frac{dx}{dy}=1.$$

Consider $y=4x^2$, $\dfrac{dy}{dx}=8x$; the inverse function is

$$x=\frac{y^{\frac{1}{2}}}{2}, \quad \text{and} \quad \frac{dx}{dy}=\frac{1}{4\sqrt{y}}=\frac{1}{4\times 2x}=\frac{1}{8x}.$$

Here again $\dfrac{dy}{dx}\times\dfrac{dx}{dy}=1.$

It can be shown that for all functions which can be put into the inverse form, one can always write

$$\frac{dy}{dx} \times \frac{dx}{dy} = 1 \quad \text{or} \quad \frac{dy}{dx} = \frac{1}{\dfrac{dx}{dy}}.$$

It follows that, being given a function, if it be easier to differentiate the inverse function, this may be done, and the reciprocal of the differential coefficient of the inverse function gives the differential coefficient of the given function itself.

As an example, suppose that we wish to differentiate $y = \sqrt[2]{\dfrac{3}{x} - 1}$. We have seen one way of doing this, by writing $u = \dfrac{3}{x} - 1$, and finding $\dfrac{dy}{du}$ and $\dfrac{du}{dx}$. This gives

$$\frac{dy}{dx} = -\frac{3}{2x^2 \sqrt{\dfrac{3}{x} - 1}}.$$

If we had forgotten how to proceed by this method, or wished to check our result by some other way of obtaining the differential coefficient, or for any other reason we could not use the ordinary method, we could proceed as follows: The inverse function is $x = \dfrac{3}{1 + y^2}$.

$$\frac{dx}{dy} = -\frac{3 \times 2y}{(1 + y^2)^2} = -\frac{6y}{(1 + y^2)^2};$$

hence $\dfrac{dy}{dx} = \dfrac{1}{\dfrac{dx}{dy}} = -\dfrac{(1 + y^2)^2}{6y} = -\dfrac{\left(1 + \dfrac{3}{x} - 1\right)^2}{6 \times \sqrt[2]{\dfrac{3}{x} - 1}} = -\dfrac{3}{2x^2 \sqrt{\dfrac{3}{x} - 1}}.$

Let us take, as another example, $y = \dfrac{1}{\sqrt[3]{\theta + 5}}$.

The inverse function $\theta = \dfrac{1}{y^3} - 5$ or $\theta = y^{-3} - 5$, and

$$\frac{d\theta}{dy} = -3y^{-4} = -3\sqrt[3]{(\theta + 5)^4}.$$

It follows that $\dfrac{dy}{d\theta} = -\dfrac{1}{3\sqrt[3]{(\theta+5)^4}}$, as might have been found otherwise.

We shall find this dodge most useful later on ; meanwhile you are advised to become familiar with it by verifying by its means the results obtained in Exercises I (p. 21), Nos. 5, 6, 7 ; Examples (pp. 58–9), Nos. 1, 2, 4 ; and Exercises VI (p. 62), Nos. 1, 2, 3 and 4.

You will surely realize from this chapter and the preceding, that in many respects the calculus is an *art* rather than a *science* : an art only to be acquired, as all other arts are, by practice. Hence you should work many examples, and set yourself other examples, to see if you can work them out, until the various artifices become familiar by use.

CHAPTER XIV

ON TRUE COMPOUND INTEREST AND THE LAW OF ORGANIC GROWTH

LET there be a quantity growing in such a way that the increment of its growth, during a given time, shall always be proportional to its own magnitude. This resembles the process of reckoning interest on money at some fixed rate ; for the bigger the capital, the bigger the amount of interest on it in a given time.

Now we must distinguish clearly between two cases, in our calculation, according as the calculation is made by what the arithmetic books call " simple interest ", or by what they call " compound interest ". For in the former case the capital remains fixed, while in the latter the interest is added to the capital, which therefore increases by successive additions.

(1) *At simple interest.* Consider a concrete case. Let the capital at start be £100, and let the rate of interest be 10 per cent. per annum. Then the increment to the owner of the capital will be £10 every year. Let him go on drawing his interest every year, and hoard it by putting it by in a stocking or locking it up in his safe. Then, if he goes on for 10 years, by the end of that time he will have received 10 increments of £10 each, or £100, making, with the original £100, a total of £200 in all. His property will have doubled itself in 10 years. If the rate of interest had been 5 per cent., he would have had to hoard for 20 years to double his property. If it had been only 2 per cent., he would have had to hoard for 50 years. It is easy to see that if the value of the yearly interest is $\frac{1}{n}$ of the capital, he must go on hoarding for n years in order to double his property.

111

Or, if y be the original capital, and the yearly interest is $\dfrac{y}{n}$, then, at the end of n years, his property will be

$$y + n\frac{y}{n} = 2y.$$

(2) *At compound interest.* As before, let the owner begin with a capital of £100, earning interest at the rate of 10 per cent. per annum ; but, instead of hoarding the interest, let it be added to the capital each year, so that the capital grows year by year. Then, at the end of one year, the capital will have grown to £110 ; and in the second year (still at 10%) this will earn £11 interest. He will start the third year with £121, and the interest on that will be £12 2s. ; so that he starts the fourth year with £133 2s., and so on. It is easy to work it out, and find that at the end of the ten years the total capital will have grown to £259 7s. 6d. In fact, we see that at the end of each year, each pound will have earned $\frac{1}{10}$ of a pound, and therefore, if this is always added on, each year multiplies the capital by $\frac{11}{10}$; and if continued for ten years (which will multiply by this factor ten times over) the original capital will be multiplied by 2·59375. Let us put this into symbols. Put y_0 for the original capital ; $\dfrac{1}{n}$ for the fraction added on at each of the n operations ; and y_n for the value of the capital at the end of the nth operation. Then

$$y_n = y_0 \left(1 + \frac{1}{n}\right)^n.$$

But this mode of reckoning compound interest once a year is really not quite fair ; for even during the first year the £100 ought to have been growing. At the end of half a year it ought to have been at least £105, and it certainly would have been fairer had the interest for the second half of the year been calculated on £105. This would be equivalent to calling it 5% per half-year ; with 20 operations, therefore, at each of which the capital is multiplied by $\frac{21}{20}$. If reckoned this way, by the end of ten years the capital would have grown to £265 8s. ; for

$$(1+\tfrac{1}{20})^{20}=2\cdot654.$$

But, even so, the process is still not quite fair ; for, by the end of the first month, there will be some interest earned ; and a half-yearly reckoning assumes that the capital remains stationary for six months at a time. Suppose we divided the year into 10 parts, and reckon a one-per-cent. interest for each tenth of the year. We now have 100 operations lasting over the ten years ; or

$$y_n=£100\,(1+\tfrac{1}{100})^{100} ;$$

which works out to £270 8s.

Even this is not final. Let the ten years be divided into 1000 periods, each of $\frac{1}{100}$ of a year ; the interest being $\frac{1}{10}$ per cent. for each such period ; then

$$y_n=£100\,(1+\tfrac{1}{1000})^{1000} ;$$

which works out to £271 14s. $2\frac{1}{2}d$.

Go even more minutely, and divide the ten years into 10,000 parts, each $\frac{1}{1000}$ of a year, with interest at $\frac{1}{100}$ of 1 per cent. Then

$$y_n=£100\,(1+\tfrac{1}{10,000})^{10,000} ;$$

which amounts to £271 16s. $4d$.

Finally, it will be seen that what we are trying to find is in reality the ultimate value of the expression $\left(1+\dfrac{1}{n}\right)^{n}$, which, as we see, is greater than 2 ; and which, as we take n larger and larger, grows closer and closer to a particular limiting value. However big you make n, the value of this expression grows nearer and nearer to the figure

$$2\cdot71828\ldots,$$

a number *never to be forgotten.*

Let us take geometrical illustrations of these things. In Fig. 36, OP stands for the original value. OT is the whole

FIG. 36.

time during which the value is growing. It is divided into 10 periods, in each of which there is an equal step up. Here $\dfrac{dy}{dx}$ is a constant; and if each step up is $\frac{1}{10}$ of the original OP, then, by 10 such steps, the height is doubled. If we had taken 20 steps, each of half the height shown, at the end the height would still be just doubled. Or n such steps, each of $\dfrac{1}{n}$ of the original height OP, would suffice to double the height. This is the case of simple interest. Here is 1 growing till it becomes 2.

In Fig. 37, we have the corresponding illustration of the geometrical progression. Each of the successive ordinates is to be $1 + \dfrac{1}{n}$, that is, $\dfrac{n+1}{n}$ times as high as its predecessor.

FIG. 37.

The steps up are not equal, because each step up is now $\frac{1}{n}$ of the ordinate *at that part* of the curve. If we had literally 10 steps, with $(1+\frac{1}{10})$ for the multiplying factor, the final total would be $(1+\frac{1}{10})^{10}$ or 2·593 times the original 1. But if only we take n sufficiently large (and the corresponding $\frac{1}{n}$ sufficiently small), then the final value $\left(1+\frac{1}{n}\right)^n$ to which unity will grow will be 2·71828.

Epsilon. To this mysterious number 2·7182818, etc., the mathematicians have assigned as a symbol the Greek letter ϵ (pronounced *epsilon*) or the English letter *e*. All schoolboys know that the Greek letter π (called *pi*) stands for 3·141592, etc. ; but how many of them know that *epsilon* means 2·71828? Yet it is an even more important number than π !

What, then, is *epsilon*?

Suppose we were to let 1 grow at simple interest till it became 2 ; then, if at the same nominal rate of interest, and for the same time, we were to let 1 grow at true compound interest, instead of simple, it would grow to the value *epsilon*.

This process of growing proportionately, at every instant, to the magnitude at that instant, some people call a *logarithmic rate* of growing. Unit logarithmic rate of growth is that rate which in unit time will cause 1 to grow to 2·718281. It might also be called the *organic rate* of growing : because it is characteristic of organic growth (in certain circumstances) that the increment of the organism in a given time is proportional to the magnitude of the organism itself.

If we take 100 per cent. as the unit of rate, and any fixed period as the unit of time, then the result of letting 1 grow *arithmetically* at unit rate, for unit time, will be 2, while the result of letting 1 grow *logarithmically* at unit rate, for the same time, will be 2·71828 ... .

A little more about Epsilon. We have seen that we require to know what value is reached by the expression $\left(1+\dfrac{1}{n}\right)^n$, when n becomes indefinitely great. Arithmetically, here are tabulated a lot of values obtained by assuming $n=2$; $n=5$; $n=10$; and so on, up to $n=10{,}000$.

$$(1+\tfrac{1}{2})^2 \qquad\qquad =2\cdot25.$$
$$(1+\tfrac{1}{5})^5 \qquad\qquad =2\cdot489.$$
$$(1+\tfrac{1}{10})^{10} \qquad\quad =2\cdot594.$$
$$(1+\tfrac{1}{20})^{20} \qquad\quad =2\cdot653.$$
$$(1+\tfrac{1}{100})^{100} \qquad =2\cdot704.$$
$$(1+\tfrac{1}{1000})^{1000} \quad\; =2\cdot7171.$$
$$(1+\tfrac{1}{10{,}000})^{10{,}000} =2\cdot7182.$$

It is, however, worth while to find another way of calculating this immensely important figure.

Accordingly, we will avail ourselves of the binomial theorem, and expand the expression $\left(1+\dfrac{1}{n}\right)^n$ in that well-known way.

The binomial theorem gives the rule that

$$(a+b)^n = a^n + n\,\frac{a^{n-1}b}{\lfloor 1}+n(n-1)\,\frac{a^{n-2}b^2}{\lfloor 2}$$
$$+n(n-1)(n-2)\,\frac{a^{n-3}b^3}{\lfloor 3}+\text{etc.}$$

Putting $a=1$ and $b=\dfrac{1}{n}$, we get

$$\left(1+\frac{1}{n}\right)^n = 1+1+\frac{1}{\lfloor 2}\left(\frac{n-1}{n}\right)+\frac{1}{\lfloor 3}\frac{(n-1)(n-2)}{n^2}$$
$$+\frac{1}{\lfloor 4}\frac{(n-1)(n-2)(n-3)}{n^3}+\text{etc.}$$

Now, if we suppose n to become indefinitely great, say a billion, or a billion billions, then $n-1$, $n-2$, and $n-3$. etc., will all be sensibly equal to n; and then the series becomes

$$\epsilon = 1 + 1 + \frac{1}{\lfloor 2} + \frac{1}{\lfloor 3} + \frac{1}{\lfloor 4} + \text{etc.} \dots .$$

By taking this rapidly convergent series to as many terms as we please, we can work out the sum to any desired point of accuracy. Here is the working for ten terms :

	1·000000
dividing by 1	1·000000
dividing by 2	0·500000
dividing by 3	0·166667
dividing by 4	0·041667
dividing by 5	0·008333
dividing by 6	0·001389
dividing by 7	0·000198
dividing by 8	0·000025
dividing by 9	0·000002
Total	2·718281

ϵ is incommensurable with 1, and resembles π in being an interminable non-recurrent decimal.

The Exponential Series. We shall have need of yet another series.

Let us, again making use of the binomial theorem, expand the expression $\left(1 + \frac{1}{n}\right)^{nx}$, which is the same as ϵ^x when we make n indefinitely great.

$$\epsilon^x = 1^{nx} + nx \frac{1^{nx-1}\left(\dfrac{1}{n}\right)}{\underline{|1}} + nx\,(nx-1)\,\frac{1^{nx-2}\left(\dfrac{1}{n}\right)^2}{\underline{|2}}$$

$$+ nx\,(nx-1)\,(nx-2)\,\frac{1^{nx-3}\left(\dfrac{1}{n}\right)^3}{\underline{|3}} + \text{etc.}$$

$$= 1 \quad + x + \frac{1}{\underline{|2}} \cdot \frac{n^2x^2 - nx}{n^2} + \frac{1}{\underline{|3}} \cdot \frac{n^3x^3 - 3n^2x^2 + 2nx}{n^3} + \text{etc.}$$

$$= 1 \quad + x + \frac{x^2 - \dfrac{x}{n}}{\underline{|2}} + \frac{x^3 - \dfrac{3x^2}{n} + \dfrac{2x}{n^2}}{\underline{|3}} + \text{etc.}$$

But, when n is made indefinitely great, this simplifies down to the following :

$$\epsilon^x = 1 + x + \frac{x^2}{\underline{|2}} + \frac{x^3}{\underline{|3}} + \frac{x^4}{\underline{|4}} + \text{etc.} \dots .$$

This series is called *the exponential series.*

The great reason why ϵ is regarded of importance is that ϵ^x possesses a property, not possessed by any other function of x, that *when you differentiate it its value remains unchanged* ; or, in other words, its differential coefficient is the same as itself. This can be instantly seen by differentiating it with respect to x, thus :

$$\frac{d\,(\epsilon^x)}{dx} = 0 + 1 + \frac{2x}{1 \cdot 2} + \frac{3x^2}{1 \cdot 2 \cdot 3} + \frac{4x^3}{1 \cdot 2 \cdot 3 \cdot 4} + \frac{5x^4}{1 \cdot 2 \cdot 3 \cdot 4 \cdot 5} + \text{etc.}$$

$$\text{or} \quad = 1 + x + \frac{x^2}{1 \cdot 2} + \frac{x^3}{1 \cdot 2 \cdot 3} + \frac{x^4}{1 \cdot 2 \cdot 3 \cdot 4} + \text{etc.,}$$

which is exactly the same as the original series.

Now we might have gone to work the other way, and said : Go to ; let us find a function of x, such that its differential coefficient is the same as itself. Or, is there any expression, involving only powers of x, which is unchanged by differentiation? Accordingly, let us *assume* as a general expression that

$$y = A + Bx + Cx^2 + Dx^3 + Ex^4 + \text{etc.},$$

(in which the coefficients A, B, C, etc., will have to be determined), and differentiate it.

$$\frac{dy}{dx} = B + 2Cx + 3Dx^2 + 4Ex^3 + \text{etc.}$$

Now, if this new expression is really to be the same as that from which it was derived, it is clear that A *must* $= B$; that $C = \dfrac{B}{2} = \dfrac{A}{1 \cdot 2}$; that $D = \dfrac{C}{3} = \dfrac{A}{1 \cdot 2 \cdot 3}$; that $E = \dfrac{D}{4} = \dfrac{A}{1 \cdot 2 \cdot 3 \cdot 4}$, etc.

The law of change is therefore that

$$y = A\left(1 + \frac{x}{1} + \frac{x^2}{1 \cdot 2} + \frac{x^3}{1 \cdot 2 \cdot 3} + \frac{x^4}{1 \cdot 2 \cdot 3 \cdot 4} + \text{etc.}\right).$$

If, now, we take $A = 1$ for the sake of further simplicity, we have

$$y = 1 + \frac{x}{1} + \frac{x^2}{1 \cdot 2} + \frac{x^3}{1 \cdot 2 \cdot 3} + \frac{x^4}{1 \cdot 2 \cdot 3 \cdot 4} + \text{etc.}$$

Differentiating it any number of times will give always the same series over again.

If, now, we take the particular case of $A = 1$, and evaluate the series, we shall get simply

when $x = 1$, $\quad y = 2 \cdot 718281$ etc. ; $\quad$ that is, $y = \epsilon$;

when $x = 2$, $\quad y = (2 \cdot 718281 \text{ etc.})^2$; $\quad$ that is, $y = \epsilon^2$;

when $x = 3$, $\quad y = (2 \cdot 718281 \text{ etc.})^3$; $\quad$ that is, $y = \epsilon^3$;

and therefore

when $x = x$, $\quad y = (2 \cdot 718281 \text{ etc.})^x$; $\quad$ that is, $y = \epsilon^x$,

thus finally demonstrating that

$$\epsilon^x = 1 + \frac{x}{1} + \frac{x^2}{1 \cdot 2} + \frac{x^3}{1 \cdot 2 \cdot 3} + \frac{x^4}{1 \cdot 2 \cdot 3 \cdot 4} + \text{etc.}$$

[NOTE.—*How to read exponentials.* For the benefit of those who have no tutor at hand it may be of use to state that ϵ^x is read as " *epsilon to the eksth power* " ; or some people read it " *exponential eks* ". So ϵ^{pt} is read " *epsilon to the pee-teeth-power* " or " *exponential pee tee* ". Take some similar expressions : Thus, ϵ^{-2} is read " *epsilon to the minus two power* " or " *exponential minus two* ". ϵ^{-ax} is read " *epsilon to the minus ay-eksth* " or " *exponential minus ay-eks* ".]

Of course it follows that ϵ^y remains unchanged if differentiated with respect to y. Also ϵ^{ax}, which is equal to $(\epsilon^a)^x$, will, when differentiated with respect to x, be $a\epsilon^{ax}$, because a is a constant.

Natural or Napierian Logarithms.

Another reason why ϵ is important is because it was made by Napier, the inventor of logarithms, the basis of his system. If y is the value of ϵ^x, then x is the *logarithm*, to the base ϵ, of y. Or, if

$$y = \epsilon^x,$$

then $$x = \log_\epsilon y.$$

The two curves plotted in Figs. 38 and 39 represent these equations.

Fig. 38.

Fig. 39.

The points calculated are :

For Fig. 38 $\Big\{$

x	0	0·5	1	1·5	2
y	1	1·65	2·71	4·50	7·69

For Fig. 39 $\Big\{$

y	1	2	3	4	8
x	0	0·69	1·10	1·39	2·08

It will be seen that, though the calculations yield different points for plotting, yet the result is identical. The two equations really mean the same thing.

As many persons who use ordinary logarithms, which are calculated to base 10 instead of base ϵ, are unfamiliar with the " natural " logarithms, it may be worth while to say a word about them. The ordinary rule that adding logarithms gives the logarithm of the product still holds good ; or

$$\log_\epsilon a + \log_\epsilon b = \log_\epsilon ab.$$

Also the rule of powers holds good ;

$$n \times \log_\epsilon a = \log_\epsilon a^n.$$

But as 10 is no longer the basis, one cannot multiply by 100 or 1000 by merely adding 2 or 3 to the index. A natural logarithm is connected to the common logarithm of the same number by the relations :

$$\log_{10} x = \log_{10} \epsilon \times \log_\epsilon x, \quad \text{and} \quad \log_\epsilon x = \log_\epsilon 10 \times \log_{10} x ;$$

But $\log_{10}\epsilon = \log_{10} \quad 2\cdot718 = 0\cdot4343, \quad \text{and} \quad \log_\epsilon 10 = 2\cdot3026 ;$

$$\therefore \quad \log_{10} x = 0\cdot4343 \times \log_\epsilon x,$$

and $\qquad\qquad \log_\epsilon x = 2\cdot3026 \times \log_{10} x.$

A Useful Table of " Naperian Logarithms " *
(Also called Natural Logarithms or Hyperbolic Logarithms)

Number	$\log_\epsilon$	Number	$\log_\epsilon$
1	0·0000	6	1·7918
1·1	0·0953	7	1·9459
1·2	0·1823	8	2·0794
1·5	0·4055	9	2·1972
1·7	0·5306	10	2·3026
2·0	0·6931	20	2·9957
2·2	0·7885	50	3·9120
2·5	0·9163	100	4·6052
2·7	0·9933	200	5·2983
2·8	1·0296	500	6·2146
3·0	1·0986	1,000	6·9078
3·5	1·2528	2,000	7·6010
4·0	1·3863	5,000	8·5172
4·5	1·5041	10,000	9·2104
5·0	1·6094	20,000	9·9035

Exponential and Logarithmic Equations.

Now let us try our hands at differentiating certain expressions that contain logarithms or exponentials.

Take the equation :

$$y = \log_\epsilon x.$$

First transform this into

$$\epsilon^y = x,$$

whence, since the differential of ϵ^y with regard to y is the original function unchanged (see p. 118),

$$\frac{dx}{dy} = \epsilon^y,$$

and, reverting from the inverse to the original function,

$$\frac{dy}{dx} = \frac{1}{\frac{dx}{dy}} = \frac{1}{\epsilon^y} = \frac{1}{x}.$$

* See Castle's *Five-Figure Logarithmic and Other Tables*, pp. 36-37, for the complete table.

Now this is a very curious result. It may be written

$$\frac{d(\log_\epsilon x)}{dx} = x^{-1}.$$

Note that x^{-1} is a result that we could never have got by the rule for differentiating powers. That rule (page 20) is to multiply by the power, and reduce the power by 1. Thus, differentiating x^3 gave us $3x^2$; and differentiating x^2 gave $2x^1$. But differentiating x^0 gives us $0 \times x^{-1} = 0$, because x^0 is itself $= 1$, and is a constant. We shall have to come back to this curious fact that differentiating $\log_\epsilon x$ gives us $\frac{1}{x}$ when we reach the chapter on integrating. (See p. 165.)

———————

Now, try to differentiate

$$y = \log_\epsilon(x+a),$$

that is $\epsilon^y = x + a$;

we have $\dfrac{d(x+a)}{dy} = e^y$, since the differential of e^y remains e^y.

This gives $\dfrac{dx}{dy} = e^y = x + a$;

hence, reverting to the original function (see p. 108), we get

$$\frac{dy}{dx} = \frac{1}{\dfrac{dx}{dy}} = \frac{1}{x+a} .$$

———————

Next try $y = \log_{10} x.$

First change to natural logarithms by multiplying by the modulus 0·4343. (See p. 121.) This gives us

$$y = 0\cdot4343 \log_\epsilon x ;$$

whence $\dfrac{dy}{dx} = \dfrac{0\cdot4343}{x} .$

———————

The next thing is not quite so simple. Try this:

$$y = a^x.$$

Taking the logarithm of both sides, we get

$$\log_\epsilon y = x \log_\epsilon a,$$

or

$$x = \frac{\log_\epsilon y}{\log_\epsilon a} = \frac{1}{\log_\epsilon a} \times \log_\epsilon y.$$

Since $\dfrac{1}{\log_\epsilon a}$ is a constant, we get

$$\frac{dx}{dy} = \frac{1}{\log_\epsilon a} \times \frac{1}{y} = \frac{1}{a^x \times \log_\epsilon a};$$

hence, reverting to the original function,

$$\frac{dy}{dx} = \frac{1}{\dfrac{dx}{dy}} = a^x \times \log_\epsilon a.$$

We see that, since

$$\frac{dx}{dy} \times \frac{dy}{dx} = 1 \quad \text{and} \quad \frac{dx}{dy} = \frac{1}{y} \times \frac{1}{\log_\epsilon a}, \quad \frac{1}{y} \times \frac{dy}{dx} = \log_\epsilon a.$$

We shall find that whenever we have an expression such as $\log_\epsilon y = $ a function of x, we always have $\dfrac{1}{y} \dfrac{dy}{dx} = $ the differential coefficient of the function of x, so that we could have written at once, from $\log_\epsilon y = x \log_\epsilon a$,

$$\frac{1}{y} \frac{dy}{dx} = \log_\epsilon a \quad \text{and} \quad \frac{dy}{dx} = y \log_\epsilon a = a^x \log_\epsilon a.$$

Let us now attempt further examples.

Examples.

(1) $y = \epsilon^{-ax}$. Let $z = -ax$; then $y = \epsilon^z$.

$$\frac{dy}{dz} = \epsilon^z; \quad \frac{dz}{dx} = -a; \quad \text{hence} \quad \frac{dy}{dx} = -a\epsilon^z = -a\epsilon^{-ax}.$$

Or thus:

$$\log_\epsilon y = -ax; \quad \frac{1}{y} \frac{dy}{dx} = -a; \quad \frac{dy}{dx} = -ay = -a\epsilon^{-ax}.$$

(2) $y = \epsilon^{\frac{x^2}{3}}$. Let $z = \dfrac{x^2}{3}$; then $y = \epsilon^z$.

$$\frac{dy}{dz} = \epsilon^z \; ; \quad \frac{dz}{dx} = \frac{2x}{3} \; ; \quad \frac{dy}{dx} = \frac{2x}{3}\,\epsilon^{\frac{x^2}{3}}.$$

Or thus : $\log_\epsilon y = \dfrac{x^2}{3}$; $\dfrac{1}{y}\dfrac{dy}{dx} = \dfrac{2x}{3}$; $\dfrac{dy}{dx} = \dfrac{2x}{3}\,\epsilon^{\frac{x^2}{3}}.$

(3) $y = \epsilon^{\frac{2x}{x+1}}$. $\log_\epsilon y = \dfrac{2x}{x+1}$, $\dfrac{1}{y}\dfrac{dy}{dx} = \dfrac{2(x+1)-2x}{(x+1)^2}$;

hence $\qquad \dfrac{dy}{dx} = \dfrac{2y}{(x+1)^2} = \dfrac{2}{(x+1)^2}\,\epsilon^{\frac{2x}{x+1}}.$

Check by writing $z = \dfrac{2x}{x+1}$.

(4) $y = \epsilon^{\sqrt{x^2+a}}$. $\log_\epsilon y = (x^2+a)^{\frac{1}{2}}$.

$$\frac{1}{y}\frac{dy}{dx} = \frac{x}{(x^2+a)^{\frac{1}{2}}} \quad \text{and} \quad \frac{dy}{dx} = \frac{x \times \epsilon^{\sqrt{x^2+a}}}{(x^2+a)^{\frac{1}{2}}}.$$

(For if $u = (x^2+a)^{\frac{1}{2}}$ and $v = x^2+a$, $u = v^{\frac{1}{2}}$,

$$\frac{du}{dv} = \frac{1}{2v^{\frac{1}{2}}} \; ; \quad \frac{dv}{dx} = 2x \; ; \quad \frac{du}{dx} = \frac{x}{(x^2+a)^{\frac{1}{2}}} \cdot \Big)$$

Check by writing $z = \sqrt{x^2+a}$.

(5) $y = \log_\epsilon(a+x^3)$. Let $z = (a+x^3)$; then $y = \log_\epsilon z$.

$$\frac{dy}{dz} = \frac{1}{z} \; ; \quad \frac{dz}{dx} = 3x^2 \; ; \quad \text{hence } \frac{dy}{dx} = \frac{3x^2}{a+x^3} \cdot$$

(6) $y = \log_\epsilon\{3x^2 + \sqrt{a+x^2}\}$. Let $z = 3x^2 + \sqrt{a+x^2}$; then $y = \log_\epsilon z$.

$$\frac{dy}{dz} = \frac{1}{z} \; ; \quad \frac{dz}{dx} = 6x + \frac{x}{\sqrt{x^2+a}} \; ;$$

$$\frac{dy}{dx} = \frac{6x + \dfrac{x}{\sqrt{x^2+a}}}{3x^2 + \sqrt{a+x^2}} = \frac{x(1 + 6\sqrt{x^2+a})}{(3x^2 + \sqrt{x^2+a})\sqrt{x^2+a}} \cdot$$

(7) $y = (x+3)^2 \sqrt{x-2}$.

$$\log_\epsilon y = 2 \log_\epsilon (x+3) + \tfrac{1}{2} \log_\epsilon (x-2).$$

$$\frac{1}{y} \frac{dy}{dx} = \frac{2}{(x+3)} + \frac{1}{2(x-2)} \;;$$

$$\frac{dy}{dx} = (x+3)^2 \sqrt{x-2} \left\{ \frac{2}{x+3} + \frac{1}{2(x-2)} \right\} = \frac{5(x+3)(x-1)}{2\sqrt{x-2}}.$$

(8) $y = (x^2+3)^3 (x^3-2)^{\frac{2}{3}}$.

$$\log_\epsilon y = 3 \log_\epsilon (x^2+3) + \tfrac{2}{3} \log_\epsilon (x^3-2) \;;$$

$$\frac{1}{y} \frac{dy}{dx} = 3 \frac{2x}{x^2+3} + \frac{2}{3} \frac{3x^2}{x^3-2} = \frac{6x}{x^2+3} + \frac{2x^2}{x^3-2}.$$

(For if $u = \log_\epsilon (x^2+3)$, $z = x^2+3$ and $u = \log_\epsilon z$.

$$\frac{du}{dz} = \frac{1}{z} \;; \quad \frac{dz}{dx} = 2x \;; \quad \frac{du}{dx} = \frac{2x}{z} = \frac{2x}{x^2+3}.$$

Similarly, if $v = \log_\epsilon (x^3-2)$, $\dfrac{dv}{dx} = \dfrac{3x^2}{x^3-2}$ and

$$\frac{dy}{dx} = (x^2+3)^3 (x^3-2)^{\frac{2}{3}} \left\{ \frac{6x}{x^2+3} + \frac{2x^2}{x^3-2} \right\}.$$

(9) $y = \dfrac{\sqrt[2]{x^2+a}}{\sqrt[3]{x^3-a}}$.

$$\log_\epsilon y = \frac{1}{2} \log_\epsilon (x^2+a) - \frac{1}{3} \log_\epsilon (x^3-a).$$

$$\frac{1}{y} \frac{dy}{dx} = \frac{1}{2} \frac{2x}{x^2+a} - \frac{1}{3} \frac{3x^2}{x^3-a} = \frac{x}{x^2+a} - \frac{x^2}{x^3-a}$$

and

$$\frac{dy}{dx} = \frac{\sqrt[2]{x^2+a}}{\sqrt[3]{x^3-a}} \left\{ \frac{x}{x^2+a} - \frac{x^2}{x^3-a} \right\}.$$

(10) $y = \dfrac{1}{\log_\epsilon x}$.

$$\frac{dy}{dx} = \frac{\log_\epsilon x \times 0 - 1 \times \dfrac{1}{x}}{\log_z{}^2 x} = -\frac{1}{x \log_\epsilon{}^2 x}.$$

(11) $y = \sqrt[3]{\log_\epsilon x} = (\log_\epsilon x)^{\frac{1}{3}}.$ Let $z = \log_\epsilon x$; $y = z^{\frac{1}{3}},$

$$\frac{dy}{dz} = \frac{1}{3} z^{-\frac{2}{3}} ; \quad \frac{dz}{dx} = \frac{1}{x} ; \quad \frac{dy}{dx} = \frac{1}{3x\sqrt[3]{\log_\epsilon{}^2 x}} .$$

(12) $y = \left(\dfrac{1}{a^x}\right)^{ax}.$

$$\log_\epsilon y = -ax \log_\epsilon a^x = -ax^2 . \log_\epsilon a.$$

$$\frac{1}{y} \frac{dy}{dx} = -2ax . \log_\epsilon a$$

and $$\frac{dy}{dx} = -2ax \left(\frac{1}{a^x}\right)^{ax} . \log_\epsilon a = -2xa^{1-ax^2} . \log_\epsilon a.$$

Try now the following exercises.

EXERCISES XII

(See page 244 for Answers)

(1) Differentiate $y = b(\epsilon^{ax} - \epsilon^{-ax}).$

(2) Find the differential coefficient with respect to t of the expression $u = at^2 + 2 \log_\epsilon t.$

(3) If $y = n^t$, find $\dfrac{d(\log_\epsilon y)}{dt}$.

(4) Show that if $y = \dfrac{1}{b} \cdot \dfrac{a^{bx}}{\log_\epsilon a}$; $\dfrac{dy}{dx} = a^{bx}.$

(5) If $w = pv^n$, find $\dfrac{dw}{dv}$.

Differentiate

(6) $y = \log_\epsilon x^n.$ **(7)** $y = 3\epsilon^{-\frac{x}{x-1}}.$ **(8)** $y = (3x^2 + 1)\epsilon^{-5x}.$

(9) $y = \log_\epsilon (x^a + a).$ **(10)** $y = (3x^2 - 1)(\sqrt{x} + 1).$

(11) $y = \dfrac{\log_\epsilon (x + 3)}{x + 3} .$ **(12)** $y = a^x \times x^a.$

(13) It was shown by Lord Kelvin that the speed of signalling through a submarine cable depends on the value of the ratio of the external diameter of the core to the diameter of the enclosed copper wire. If this ratio is called y, then the number of signals s that can be sent per minute can be expressed by the formula

$$s = ay^2 \log_\epsilon \frac{1}{y} \; ;$$

where a is a constant depending on the length and the quality of the materials. Show that if these are given, s will be a maximum if $y = 1 \div \sqrt{\epsilon}$.

(14) Find the maximum or minimum of

$$y = x^3 - \log_\epsilon x.$$

(15) Differentiate $y = \log_\epsilon (ax\epsilon^x)$.

(16) Differentiate $y = (\log_\epsilon ax)^3$.

The Logarithmic Curve

Let us return to the curve which has its successive ordinates in geometrical progression, such as that represented by the equation $y = bp^x$.

We can see, by putting $x = 0$, that b is the initial height of y. Then when

$$x = 1, \; y = bp \; ; \quad x = 2, \; y = bp^2 \; ; \quad x = 3, \; y = bp^3, \text{ etc.}$$

Also, we see that p is the numerical value of the ratio between the height of any ordinate and that of the next preceding it. In Fig. 40, we have taken p as $\frac{6}{5}$; each ordinate being $\frac{6}{5}$ as high as the preceding one.

If two successive ordinates are related together thus in a constant ratio, their logarithms will have a constant difference; so

Fig. 40.

that, if we should plot out a new curve, Fig. 41, with values of $\log_\epsilon y$ as ordinates, it would be a straight line sloping up by equal steps. In fact, it follows from the equation, that

$$\log_\epsilon y = \log_\epsilon b + x \cdot \log_\epsilon p, \quad \text{whence} \quad \log_\epsilon y - \log_\epsilon b = x \cdot \log_\epsilon p.$$

FIG. 41.

Now, since $\log_\epsilon p$ is a mere number, and may be written as $\log_\epsilon p = a$, it follows that

$$\log_\epsilon \frac{y}{b} = ax,$$

and the equation takes the new form

$$y = b\epsilon^{ax}.$$

The Die-away Curve

If we were to take p as a proper fraction (less than unity), the curve would obviously tend to sink downwards, as in Fig. 42, where each successive ordinate is ¾ of the height of the preceding one.

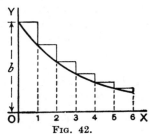

FIG. 42.

The equation is still

$$y = bp^x \; ;$$

but since p is less than one, $\log_\epsilon p$ will be a negative quantity, and may be written $-a$; so that $p = \epsilon^{-a}$, and now our equation for the curve takes the form

$$y = b\epsilon^{-ax}.$$

The importance of this expression is that, in the case where the independent variable is *time*, the equation represents the course of a great many physical processes in which something is *gradually dying away*. Thus, the cooling of a hot body is represented (in Newton's celebrated " law of cooling ") by the equation

$$\theta_t = \theta_0 \epsilon^{-at} \; ;$$

where θ_0 is the original excess of temperature of a hot body over that of its surroundings, θ_t the excess of temperature at the end of time t, and a is a constant—namely, the constant of decrement, depending on the amount of surface exposed by the body, and on its coefficients of conductivity and emissivity, etc.

A similar formula,

$$Q_t = Q_0 \epsilon^{-at},$$

is used to express the charge of an electrified body, originally having a charge Q_0, which is leaking away with a constant of decrement a ; which constant depends in this case on the capacity of the body and on the resistance of the leakage-path.

Oscillations given to a flexible spring die out after a time ; and the dying-out of the amplitude of the motion may be expressed in a similar way.

In fact ϵ^{-at} serves as a *die-away factor* for all those phenomena in which the rate of decrease is proportional to the magnitude of that which is decreasing ; or where, in our usual symbols, $\dfrac{dy}{dt}$ is proportional at every moment to the value that

y has at that moment. For we have only to inspect the curve, Fig. 42 (p. 129), to see that, at every part of it, the slope $\dfrac{dy}{dx}$ is proportional to the height y; the curve becoming flatter as y grows smaller. In symbols, thus

$$y = b\epsilon^{-ax}$$

or $$\log_\epsilon y = \log_\epsilon b - ax \log_\epsilon \epsilon = \log_\epsilon b - ax,$$

and, differentiating, $$\frac{1}{y}\frac{dy}{dx} = -a ;$$

hence $$\frac{dy}{dx} = b\epsilon^{-ax} \times (-a) = -ay ;$$

or, in words, the slope of the curve is downward, and proportional to y and to the constant a.

We should have got the same result if we had taken the equation in the form

$$y = bp^x ;$$

for then $$\frac{dy}{dx} = bp^x \times \log_\epsilon p.$$

But $$\log_\epsilon p = -a ;$$

giving us $$\frac{dy}{dx} = y \times (-a) = -ay,$$

as before.

The Time-constant. In the expression for the " die-away factor " ϵ^{-at}, the quantity a is the reciprocal of another quantity known as " *the time-constant* ", which we may denote by the symbol T. Then the die-away factor will be written $\epsilon^{-\frac{t}{T}}$; and it will be seen, by making $t = T$, that the meaning of T $\left(\text{or of } \dfrac{1}{a}\right)$ is that this is the length of time which it takes for the original quantity (called θ_0 or Q_0 in the preceding instances) to die away to $\dfrac{1}{\epsilon}$th part—that is to $0\cdot3678$—of its original value.

K

The values of ϵ^x and ϵ^{-x} are continually required in different branches of physics, and as they are given in very few sets of mathematical tables, some of the values are tabulated here for convenience.*

x	ϵ^x	ϵ^{-x}	$1 - \epsilon^{-x}$
0·00	1·0000	1·0000	0·0000
0·10	1·1052	0·9048	0·0952
0·20	1·2214	0·8187	0·1813
0·50	1·6487	0·6065	0·3935
0·75	2·1170	0·4724	0·5276
0·90	2·4596	0·4066	0·5934
1·00	2·7183	0·3679	0·6321
1·10	3·0042	0·3329	0·6671
1·20	3·3201	0·3012	0·6988
1·25	3·4903	0·2865	0·7135
1·50	4·4817	0·2231	0·7769
1·75	5·754	0·1738	0·8262
2·00	7·389	0·1353	0·8647
2·50	12·183	0·0821	0·9179
3·00	20·085	0·0498	0·9502
3·50	33·115	0·0302	0·9698
4·00	54·598	0·0183	0·9817
4·50	90·017	0·0111	0·9889
5·00	148·41	0·0067	0·9933
5·50	244·69	0·0041	0·9959
6·00	403·43	0·00248	0·99752
7·50	1808·04	0·00053	0·99947
10·00	22026·5	0·000045	0·999955

As an example of the use of this table, suppose there is a hot body cooling, and that at the beginning of the experiment (*i.e.* when $t = 0$) it is 72° hotter than the surrounding objects, and if the time-constant of its cooling is 20 minutes (that is, if it takes 20 minutes for its excess of temperature to fall to $\frac{1}{\epsilon}$ part of 72°), then we can calculate to what it will have fallen

* See Castle's *Five-Figure Logarithmic and Other Tables*, p. 60.

in any given time t. For instance, let t be 60 minutes. Then $\frac{t}{T} = 60 \div 20 = 3$, and we shall have to find the value of ϵ^{-3}, and then multiply the original 72° by this. The table shows that ϵ^{-3} is 0·0498. So that at the end of 60 minutes the excess of temperature will have fallen to $72° \times 0·0498 = 3·586°$.

Further Examples.

(1) The strength of an electric current in a conductor at a time t secs. after the application of the electromotive force producing it is given by the expression $C = \frac{E}{R}\left\{ 1 - \epsilon^{-\frac{Rt}{L}} \right\}$.

The time constant is $\frac{L}{R}$.

If $E = 10$, $R = 1$, $L = 0·01$; then when t is very large the term $1 - \epsilon^{-\frac{Rt}{L}}$ becomes 1, and $C = \frac{E}{R} = 10$; also

$$\frac{L}{R} = T = 0·01.$$

Its value at any time may be written :

$$C = 10 - 10\epsilon^{-\frac{t}{0·01}},$$

the time-constant being 0·01. This means that it takes 0·01 sec. for the variable term to fall to $\frac{1}{\epsilon} = 0·3678$ of its initial value $10\epsilon^{-\frac{0}{0·01}} = 10$.

To find the value of the current when $t = 0·001$ sec., say, $\frac{t}{T} = 0·1$, $\epsilon^{-0·1} = 0·9048$ (from table).

It follows that, after 0·001 sec., the variable term is

$$0·9048 \times 10 = 9·048,$$

and the actual current is $10 - 9·048 = 0·952$.

Similarly, at the end of 0·1 sec.,

$$\frac{t}{T} = 10 \; ; \quad \epsilon^{-10} = 0\cdot000045 \; ;$$

the variable term is $10 \times 0\cdot000045 = 0\cdot00045$, the current being 9·9995.

(2) The intensity I of a beam of light which has passed through a thickness l cm. of some transparent medium is $I = I_0\epsilon^{-Kl}$, where I_0 is the initial intensity of the beam and K is a " constant of absorption ".

This constant is usually found by experiments. If it be found, for instance, that a beam of light has its intensity diminished by 18% in passing through 10 cm. of a certain transparent medium, this means that $82 = 100 \times \epsilon^{-K \times 10}$ or $\epsilon^{-10K} = 0\cdot82$, and from the table one sees that $10K = 0\cdot20$ very nearly ; hence $K = 0\cdot02$.

To find the thickness that will reduce the intensity to half its value, one must find the value of l which satisfies the equality $50 = 100 \times \epsilon^{-0\cdot02l}$, or $0\cdot5 = \epsilon^{-0\cdot02l}$. It is found by putting this equation in its logarithmic form, namely,

$$\log 0\cdot5 = -0\cdot02 \times l \times \log \epsilon,$$

which gives

$$l = \frac{\bar{1}\cdot6990}{-0\cdot02 \times 0\cdot4343} = \frac{-0\cdot3010}{-0\cdot008686} = 34\cdot7 \text{ cm. nearly.}$$

(3) The quantity Q of a radio-active substance which has not yet undergone transformation is known to be related to the initial quantity Q_0 of the substance by the relation $Q = Q_0\epsilon^{-\lambda t}$, where λ is a constant and t the time in seconds elapsed since the transformation began.

For " Radium A ", if time is expressed in seconds, experiment shows that $\lambda = 3\cdot85 \times 10^{-3}$. Find the time required for transforming half the substance. (This time is called the " mean life " of the substance.)

We have $\qquad 0\cdot5 = \epsilon^{-0\cdot00385t}$.

$$\log 0\cdot5 = -0\cdot00385t \times \log \epsilon\ ;$$

and $\qquad\qquad\qquad t = 3$ minutes very nearly.

EXERCISES XIII.

(See page 245 for Answers)

(1) Draw the curve $y = b\epsilon^{-\frac{t}{T}}$; where $b = 12$, $T = 8$, and t is given various values from 0 to 20.

(2) If a hot body cools so that in 24 minutes its excess of temperature has fallen to half the initial amount, deduce the time-constant, and find how long it will be in cooling down to 1 per cent. of the original excess.

(3) Plot the curve $y = 100(1 - \epsilon^{-2t})$.

(4) The following equations give very similar curves :

$$\text{(i)}\ \ y = \frac{ax}{x+b}\ ;\quad \text{(ii)}\ \ y = a\left(1 - \epsilon^{-\frac{x}{b}}\right)\ ;$$
$$\text{(iii)}\ \ y = \frac{a}{90°}\ \text{arc tan}\left(\frac{x}{b}\right).$$

Draw all three curves, taking $a = 100$ millimetres; $b = 30$ millimetres.

(5) Find the differential coefficient of y with respect to x, if

$$\text{(a)}\ \ y = x^x\ ;\quad \text{(b)}\ \ y = (\epsilon^x)^x\ ;\quad \text{(c)}\ \ y = \epsilon^{x^x}.$$

(6) For " Thorium A ", the value of λ is 5 ; find the " mean life ", that is, the time taken by the transformation of a quantity Q of " Thorium A " equal to half the initial quantity Q_0 in the expression

$$Q = Q_0\epsilon^{-\lambda t}\ ;$$

t being in seconds.

(7) A condenser of capacity $K = 4 \times 10^{-6}$, charged to a potential $V_0 = 20$, is discharging through a resistance of 10,000 ohms. Find the potential V after (a) 0·1 second ; (b) 0·01 second ; assuming that the fall of potential follows the rule $V = V_0 \epsilon^{-\frac{t}{KR}}$.

(8) The charge Q of an electrified insulated metal sphere is reduced from 20 to 16 units in 10 minutes. Find the coefficient μ of leakage, if $Q = Q_0 \times \epsilon^{-\mu t}$; Q_0 being the initial charge and t being in seconds. Hence find the time taken by half the charge to leak away.

(9) The damping on a telephone line can be ascertained from the relation $i = i_0 \epsilon^{-\beta l}$, where i is the strength, after t seconds, of a telephonic current of initial strength i_0 ; l is the length of the line in kilometres, and β is a constant. For the Franco-English submarine cable laid in 1910, $\beta = 0·0114$. Find the damping at the end of the cable (40 kilometres), and the length along which i is still 8% of the original current (limiting value of very good audition).

(10) The pressure p of the atmosphere at an altitude h kilometres is given by $p = p_0 \epsilon^{-kh}$; p_0 being the pressure at sea-level (760 millimetres).

The pressures at 10, 20 and 50 kilometres being 199·2, 42·2, 0·32 millimetres respectively, find k in each case. Using the mean value of k, find the percentage error in each case.

(11) Find the minimum or maximum of $y = x^x$.

(12) Find the minimum or maximum of $y = x^{\frac{1}{x}}$.

(13) Find the minimum or maximum of $y = xa^{\frac{1}{x}}$.

CHAPTER XV

HOW TO DEAL WITH SINES AND COSINES

GREEK letters being usual to denote angles, we will take as the usual letter for any variable angle the letter θ (" theta ").

Let us consider the function

$$y = \sin \theta.$$

What we have to investigate is the value of $\dfrac{d(\sin \theta)}{d\theta}$; or, in other words, if the angle θ varies, we have to find the relation between the increment of the sine and the increment of the angle, both increments being indefinitely small in themselves. Examine Fig. 43, wherein, if the radius of the circle is unity,

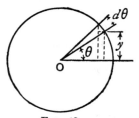

FIG. 43.

the height of y is the sine, and θ is the angle. Now, if θ is supposed to increase by the addition to it of the small angle $d\theta$—an element of angle—the height of y, the sine, will be increased by a small element dy. The new height $y + dy$ will be the sine of the new angle $\theta + d\theta$, or, stating it as an equation,

$$y + dy = \sin (\theta + d\theta) \; ;$$

and subtracting from this the first equation gives

$$dy = \sin (\theta + d\theta) - \sin \theta.$$

The quantity on the right-hand side is the difference between two sines, and books on trigonometry tell us how to work this out. For they tell us that if M and N are two different angles,

$$\sin M - \sin N = 2 \cos \frac{M+N}{2} \cdot \sin \frac{M-N}{2}.$$

If, then, we put $M = \theta + d\theta$ for one angle, and $N = \theta$ for the other, we may write

$$dy = 2 \cos \frac{\theta + d\theta + \theta}{2} \cdot \sin \frac{\theta + d\theta - \theta}{2},$$

or, $$dy = 2 \cos (\theta + \tfrac{1}{2}d\theta) \cdot \sin \tfrac{1}{2}d\theta.$$

But if we regard $d\theta$ as indefinitely small, then in the limit we may neglect $\tfrac{1}{2}d\theta$ by comparison with θ, and may also take $\sin \tfrac{1}{2}d\theta$ as being the same as $\tfrac{1}{2}d\theta$. The equation then becomes :

$$dy = 2 \cos \theta \times \tfrac{1}{2}d\theta ;$$
$$dy = \cos \theta \cdot d\theta,$$

and, finally, $$\frac{dy}{d\theta} = \cos \theta.$$

The accompanying curves, Figs. 44 and 45, show, plotted to scale, the values of $y = \sin \theta$, and $\frac{dy}{d\theta} = \cos \theta$, for the corresponding values of θ.

Fig. 44.

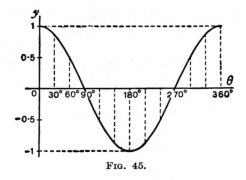

FIG. 45.

Take next the cosine.

Let $y = \cos \theta$.

Now $\cos \theta = \sin \left(\dfrac{\pi}{2} - \theta \right)$.

Therefore

$$dy = d \left(\sin \left(\frac{\pi}{2} - \theta \right) \right) = \cos \left(\frac{\pi}{2} - \theta \right) \times d(-\theta),$$

$$= \cos \left(\frac{\pi}{2} - \theta \right) \times (-d\theta),$$

$$\frac{dy}{d\theta} = -\cos \left(\frac{\pi}{2} - \theta \right).$$

And it follows that

$$\frac{dy}{d\theta} = -\sin \theta.$$

Lastly, take the tangent.

Let $$y = \tan \theta$$

$$= \frac{\sin \theta}{\cos \theta}.$$

The differential coefficient of $\sin \theta$ is $\dfrac{d(\sin \theta)}{d\theta}$, and the differential coefficient of $\cos \theta$ is $\dfrac{d(\cos \theta)}{d\theta}$. Applying the rule given on page 35 for differentiating a quotient of two functions, we get

$$\frac{dy}{d\theta} = \frac{\cos \theta \dfrac{d(\sin \theta)}{d\theta} - \sin \theta \dfrac{d(\cos \theta)}{d\theta}}{\cos^2\theta}$$

$$= \frac{\cos^2\theta + \sin^2\theta}{\cos^2\theta}$$

$$= \frac{1}{\cos^2\theta},$$

or $$\frac{dy}{d\theta} = \sec^2\theta.$$

Collecting these results, we have :

y	$\dfrac{dy}{d\theta}$
$\sin \theta$	$\cos \theta$
$\cos \theta$	$-\sin \theta$
$\tan \theta$	$\sec^2\theta$

Sometimes, in mechanical and physical questions, as, for example, in simple harmonic motion and in wave-motions, we have to deal with angles that increase in proportion to the time. Thus, if T be the time of one complete *period*, or movement round the circle, then, since the angle all round the circle is 2π radians, or $360°$, the amount of angle moved through in time t will be

$$\theta = 2\pi \frac{t}{T}, \text{ in radians,}$$

or $$\theta = 360 \frac{t}{T}, \text{ in degrees.}$$

If the *frequency*, or number of periods per second, be denoted by n, then $n = \frac{1}{T}$, and we may then write :

$$\theta = 2\pi nt.$$

Then we shall have $\qquad y = \sin 2\pi nt.$

If, now, we wish to know how the sine varies with respect to time, we must differentiate with respect, not to θ, but to t. For this we must resort to the artifice explained in Chapter IX, p. 57, and put

$$\frac{dy}{dt} = \frac{dy}{d\theta} \cdot \frac{d\theta}{dt}.$$

Now $\frac{d\theta}{dt}$ will obviously be $2\pi n$; so that

$$\frac{dy}{dt} = \cos \theta \times 2\pi n$$

$$= 2\pi n \cdot \cos 2\pi nt$$

Similarly, it follows that

$$\frac{d(\cos 2\pi nt)}{dt} = -2\pi n \cdot \sin 2\pi nt.$$

Second Differential Coefficient of Sine or Cosine

We have seen that when $\sin \theta$ is differentiated with respect to θ it becomes $\cos \theta$; and that when $\cos \theta$ is differentiated with respect to θ it becomes $-\sin \theta$; or, in symbols,

$$\frac{d^2(\sin \theta)}{d\theta^2} = -\sin \theta.$$

So we have this curious result that we have found a function such that if we differentiate it twice over, we get the same thing from which we started, but with the sign changed from $+$ to $-$.

The same thing is true for the cosine ; for differentiating $\cos \theta$ gives us $-\sin \theta$, and differentiating $-\sin \theta$ gives us $-\cos \theta$; or thus :

$$\frac{d^2(\cos \theta)}{d\theta^2} = -\cos \theta.$$

Sines and cosines are the only functions of which the second differential coefficient is equal and of opposite sign to the original function.

Examples.

With what we have so far learned we can now differentiate expressions of a more complex nature.

(1) $y = \text{arc} \sin x$.

If y is the arc whose sine is x, then $x = \sin y$.

$$\frac{dx}{dy} = \cos y.$$

Passing now from the inverse function to the original one, we get

$$\frac{dy}{dx} = \frac{1}{\dfrac{dx}{dy}} = \frac{1}{\cos y}.$$

Now　　　　　　$\cos y = \sqrt{1 - \sin^2 y} = \sqrt{1 - x^2}$;

hence　　　　　　$\dfrac{dy}{dx} = \dfrac{1}{\sqrt{1 - x^2}}$,

a rather unexpected result.

(2) $y = \cos^3 \theta$.

This is the same thing as $y = (\cos \theta)^3$.

Let $v = \cos \theta$; then $y = v^3$; $\dfrac{dy}{dv} = 3v^2$.

$$\frac{dv}{d\theta} = -\sin \theta.$$

$$\frac{dy}{d\theta} = \frac{dy}{dv} \times \frac{dv}{d\theta} = -3\cos^2\theta \sin \theta.$$

(3) $y = \sin(x + a)$.

Let $v = x + a$; then $y = \sin v$.

$$\frac{dv}{dx} = 1; \quad \frac{dy}{dv} = \cos v \quad \text{and} \quad \frac{dy}{dx} = \cos(x + a).$$

(4) $y = \log_\epsilon \sin \theta$.

Let $v = \sin \theta$; $y = \log_\epsilon v$.

$$\frac{dv}{d\theta} = \cos \theta; \quad \frac{dy}{dv} = \frac{1}{v}; \quad \frac{dy}{d\theta} = \frac{1}{\sin \theta} \times \cos \theta = \cot \theta.$$

(5) $y = \cot \theta = \dfrac{\cos \theta}{\sin \theta}$.

$$\frac{dy}{d\theta} = \frac{-\sin^2\theta - \cos^2\theta}{\sin^2\theta}$$

$$= -(1 + \cot^2\theta) = -\operatorname{cosec}^2\theta.$$

(6) $y = \tan 3\theta$.

Let $v = 3\theta$; $y = \tan v$; $\dfrac{dv}{d\theta} = 3$; $\dfrac{dy}{dv} = \sec^2 v$;

and
$$\frac{dy}{d\theta} = 3 \sec^2 3\theta.$$

(7) $y = \sqrt{1 + 3\tan^2\theta} = (1 + 3\tan^2\theta)^{\frac{1}{2}}$.

Let $v = 3\tan^2\theta$, then $y = (1 + v)^{\frac{1}{2}}$;

$$\therefore \frac{dv}{d\theta} = 6\tan\theta\sec^2\theta; \quad \frac{dy}{dv} = \frac{1}{2\sqrt{1 + v}} \text{ (see p. 58)};$$

and
$$\frac{dy}{d\theta} = \frac{6\tan\theta\sec^2\theta}{2\sqrt{1 + v}} = \frac{6\tan\theta\sec^2\theta}{2\sqrt{1 + 3\tan^2\theta}}.$$

(for, if $u = \tan\theta$, $v = 3u^2$;

$$\frac{du}{d\theta} = \sec^2\theta; \quad \frac{dv}{du} = 6u;$$

hence
$$\frac{dv}{d\theta} = 6\tan\theta\sec^2\theta;$$

hence
$$\frac{dy}{d\theta} = \frac{6\tan\theta\sec^2\theta}{2\sqrt{1 + 3\tan^2\theta}}\Bigg).$$

(8) $y = \sin x \cos x$.

$$\frac{dy}{dx} = \sin x (-\sin x) + \cos x \times \cos x$$
$$= \cos^2 x - \sin^2 x.$$

Closely associated with *sines, cosines* and *tangents* are three other very useful functions. They are the hyperbolic sine, cosine and tangent, and are written *sinh, cosh, tanh.* These functions are defined as follows :

$$\sinh x = \tfrac{1}{2}(\epsilon^x - \epsilon^{-x}), \quad \cosh x = \tfrac{1}{2}(\epsilon^x + \epsilon^{-x}),$$
$$\tanh x = \frac{\sinh x}{\cosh x} = \frac{\epsilon^x - \epsilon^{-x}}{\epsilon^x + \epsilon^{-x}}.$$

Between $\sinh x$ and $\cosh x$, there is an important relation, for
$$\cosh^2 x - \sinh^2 x = \tfrac{1}{4}(\epsilon^x + \epsilon^{-x})^2 - \tfrac{1}{4}(\epsilon^x - \epsilon^{-x})^2$$
$$= \tfrac{1}{4}(\epsilon^{2x} + 2 + \epsilon^{-2x} - \epsilon^{2x} + 2 - \epsilon^{-2x}) = 1.$$

Now $\dfrac{d}{dx}(\sinh x) = \tfrac{1}{2}(\epsilon^x + \epsilon^{-x}) = \cosh x.$ (See p. 118.)

$$\frac{d}{dx}(\cosh x) = \tfrac{1}{2}(\epsilon^x - \epsilon^{-x}) = \sinh x,$$

$$\frac{d}{dx}(\tanh x) = \frac{\cosh x \dfrac{d}{dx}(\sinh x) - \sinh x \dfrac{d}{dx}(\cosh x)}{\cosh^2 x}$$

$$= \frac{\cosh^2 x - \sinh^2 x}{\cosh^2 x} = \frac{1}{\cosh^2 x}$$

by the relation just proved.

EXERCISES XIV

(See page 245 for Answers)

(1) Differentiate the following :

(i) $y = A \sin\left(\theta - \dfrac{\pi}{2}\right).$

(ii) $y = \sin^2\theta$; and $y = \sin 2\theta.$

(iii) $y = \sin^3\theta$: and $y = \sin 3\theta.$

(2) Find the value of θ for which $\sin \theta \times \cos \theta$ is a maximum.

(3) Differentiate $y = \dfrac{1}{2\pi} \cos 2\pi nt$.

(4) If $y = \sin a^x$, find $\dfrac{dy}{dx}$.   (5) Differentiate $y = \log_\epsilon \cos x$.

(6) Differentiate $y = 18 \cdot 2 \sin (x + 26°)$.

(7) Plot the curve $y = 100 \sin (\theta - 15°)$; and show that the slope of the curve at $\theta = 75°$ is half the maximum slope.

(8) If $y = \sin \theta \cdot \sin 2\theta$, find $\dfrac{dy}{d\theta}$.

(9) If $y = a \cdot \tan^m (\theta^n)$, find the differential coefficient of y with respect to θ.

(10) Differentiate $y = \epsilon^x \sin^2 x$.

(11) Differentiate the three equations of Exercises XIII (p. 135), No. 4, and compare their differential coefficients, as to whether they are equal, or nearly equal, for very small values of x, or for very large values of x, or for values of x in the neighbourhood of $x = 30$.

(12) Differentiate the following :

(i) $y = \sec x$.   (ii) $y = \text{arc } \cos x$.

(iii) $y = \text{arc } \tan x$.   (iv) $y = \text{arc } \sec x$.

(v) $y = \tan x \times \sqrt{3 \sec x}$.

(13) Differentiate $y = \sin (2\theta + 3)^{2 \cdot 3}$.

(14) Differentiate $y = \theta^3 + 3 \sin (\theta + 3) - 3^{\sin \theta} - 3^\theta$.

(15) Find the maximum or minimum of $y = \theta \cos \theta$.

(Now try Ex. 4–8, on page 64.)

CHAPTER XVI

PARTIAL DIFFERENTIATION

WE sometimes come across quantities that are functions of more than one independent variable. Thus, we may find a case where y depends on two other variable quantities, one of which we will call u and the other v. In symbols

$$y = f(u, v).$$

Take the simplest concrete case.

Let $\qquad\qquad y = u \times v.$

What are we to do? If we were to treat v as a constant, and differentiate with respect to u, we should get

$$dy_v = v \, du \; ;$$

or if we treat u as a constant, and differentiate with respect to v, we should have :

$$dy_u = u \, dv.$$

The little letters here put as subscripts are to show which quantity has been taken as constant in the operation.

Another way of indicating that the differentiation has been performed only *partially*, that is, has been performed only with respect to *one* of the independent variables, is to write the differential coefficients with Greek deltas, like ∂, instead of little d. In this way

$$\frac{\partial y}{\partial u} = v,$$

$$\frac{\partial y}{\partial v} = u.$$

If we put in these values for v and u respectively, we shall have

$$\left.\begin{aligned} dy_v &= \frac{\partial y}{\partial u}\, du, \\ dy_u &= \frac{\partial y}{\partial v}\, dv, \end{aligned}\right\} \text{ which are } \textit{partial differentials.}$$

But, if you think of it, you will observe that the total variation of y depends on *both* these things at the same time. That is to say, if both are varying, the real dy ought to be written

$$dy = \frac{\partial y}{\partial u}\, du + \frac{\partial y}{\partial v}\, dv\,;$$

and this is called a *total differential*. In some books it is written $dy = \left(\dfrac{dy}{du}\right) du + \left(\dfrac{dy}{dv}\right) dv$.

Example (1). Find the partial differential coefficients of the expression $w = 2ax^2 + 3bxy + 4cy^3$. The answers are :

$$\left.\begin{aligned} \frac{\partial w}{\partial x} &= 4ax + 3by. \\ \frac{\partial w}{\partial y} &= 3bx + 12cy^2. \end{aligned}\right\}$$

The first is obtained by supposing y constant, the second is obtained by supposing x constant ; then

$$dw = (4ax + 3by)\, dx + (3bx + 12cy^2)\, dy.$$

Example (2). Let $z = x^y$. Then, treating first y and then x as constant, we get in the usual way

$$\left.\begin{aligned} \frac{\partial z}{\partial x} &= yx^{y-1}, \\ \frac{\partial z}{\partial y} &= x^y \times \log_\epsilon x, \end{aligned}\right\}$$

so that $dz = yx^{y-1} dx + x^y \log_\epsilon x\, dy$.

Example (3). A cone having height h and radius of base r, has volume $V = \frac{1}{3}\pi r^2 h$. If its height remains constant, while r changes, the ratio of change of volume, with respect to radius, is different from ratio of change of volume with respect to height which would occur if the height were varied and the radius kept constant, for

$$\left. \begin{array}{l} \dfrac{\partial V}{\partial r} = \dfrac{2\pi}{3}\, rh, \\[2mm] \dfrac{\partial V}{\partial h} = \dfrac{\pi}{3}\, r^2. \end{array} \right\}$$

The variation when both the radius and the height change is given by $dV = \dfrac{2\pi}{3}\, rh\, dr + \dfrac{\pi}{3}\, r^2 dh.$

Example (4). In the following example F and f denote two arbitrary functions of any form whatsoever. For example, they may be sine-functions, or exponentials, or mere algebraic functions of the two independent variables, t and x. This being understood, let us take the expression

$$y = F(x + at) + f(x - at),$$

or, $\qquad y = F(w) + f(v) \cdot$

where $\qquad w = x + at, \quad \text{and} \quad v = x - at.$

Then $\qquad \dfrac{dy}{dx} = \dfrac{\partial F(w)}{\partial w} \cdot \dfrac{dw}{dx} + \dfrac{\partial f(v)}{\partial v} \cdot \dfrac{dv}{dx}$

$$= F'(w) \cdot 1 + f'(v) \cdot 1$$

(where the figure 1 is simply the coefficient of x in w and v) ;

and $\qquad \dfrac{d^2 y}{dx^2} = F''(w) + f''(v).$

Also $\qquad \dfrac{dy}{dt} = \dfrac{\partial F(w)}{\partial w} \cdot \dfrac{dw}{dt} + \dfrac{\partial f(v)}{\partial v} \cdot \dfrac{dv}{dt}$

$$= F'(w) \cdot a - f'(v)a \; ;$$

and
$$\frac{d^2y}{dt^2} = F''(w)a^2 + f''(v)a^2 \; ;$$

whence
$$\frac{d^2y}{dt^2} = a^2 \frac{d^2y}{dx^2}.$$

This differential equation is of immense importance in mathematical physics.   (See also page 206.)

Maxima and Minima of Functions of two Independent Variables

Example (5).   Let us take up again Exercises IX, p. 91, No. 4.

Let x and y be the length of two of the portions of the string.   The third is $30 - (x+y)$, and the area of the triangle is $A = \sqrt{s(s-x)(s-y)(s-30+x+y)}$, where s is the half perimeter, so that $s = 15$, and $A = \sqrt{15P}$, where

$$P = (15-x)(15-y)(x+y-15)$$
$$= xy^2 + x^2y - 15x^2 - 15y^2 - 45xy + 450x + 450y - 3375.$$

Clearly A is maximum when P is maximum.

$$dP = \frac{\partial P}{\partial x} dx + \frac{\partial P}{\partial y} dy.$$

For a maximum (clearly it will not be a minimum in this case), one must have simultaneously

$$\frac{\partial P}{\partial x} = 0 \quad \text{and} \quad \frac{\partial P}{\partial y} = 0 \; ;$$

that is,
$$\left. \begin{array}{l} 2xy - 30x + y^2 - 45y + 450 = 0, \\ 2xy - 30y + x^2 - 45x + 450 = 0. \end{array} \right\}$$

An immediate solution is $x = y$.

If we now introduce this condition in the value of P, we find

$$P = (15-x)^2(2x-15) = 2x^3 - 75x^2 + 900x - 3375.$$

For maximum or minimum, $\dfrac{dP}{dx} = 6x^2 - 150x + 900 = 0$, which gives $x = 15$ or $x = 10$.

Clearly $x = 15$ gives zero area; $x = 10$ gives the maximum, for $\dfrac{d^2P}{dx^2} = 12x - 150$, which is $+30$ for $x = 15$ and -30 for $x = 10$.

Example (6). Find the dimensions of an ordinary railway coal truck with rectangular ends, so that, for a given volume V, the area of sides and floor together is as small as possible.

The truck is a rectangular box open at the top. Let x be the length and y be the width; then the depth is $\dfrac{V}{xy}$. The surface area is $S = xy + \dfrac{2V}{x} + \dfrac{2V}{y}$.

$$dS = \frac{\partial S}{\partial x}\,dx + \frac{\partial S}{\partial y}\,dy = \left(y - \frac{2V}{x^2}\right)dx + \left(x - \frac{2V}{y^2}\right)dy.$$

For minimum (clearly it won't be a maximum here),

$$y - \frac{2V}{x^2} = 0, \quad x - \frac{2V}{y^2} = 0.$$

Here also, an immediate solution is $x = y$, so that $S = x^2 + \dfrac{4V}{x}$, $\dfrac{dS}{dx} = 2x - \dfrac{4V}{x^2} = 0$ for minimum, and $x = \sqrt[3]{2V}$.

EXERCISES XV

(*See page 246 for Answers*)

(1) Differentiate the expression $\dfrac{x^3}{3} - 2x^3y - 2y^2x + \dfrac{y}{3}$ with respect to x alone, and with respect to y alone.

(2) Find the partial differential coefficients with respect to x, y and z, of the expression

$$x^2yz + xy^2z + xyz^2 + x^2y^2z^2.$$

(3) Let $r^2 = (x-a)^2 + (y-b)^2 + (z-c)^2$.

Find the value of $\dfrac{\partial r}{\partial x} + \dfrac{\partial r}{\partial y} + \dfrac{\partial r}{\partial z}$. Also find the value of $\dfrac{\partial^2 r}{\partial x^2} + \dfrac{\partial^2 r}{\partial y^2} + \dfrac{\partial^2 r}{\partial z^2}$.

(4) Find the total differential of $y = u^v$.

(5) Find the total differential of $y = u^3 \sin v$; of $y = (\sin x)^u$; and of $y = \dfrac{\log_\epsilon u}{v}$.

(6) Verify that the sum of three quantities x, y, z, whose product is a constant k, is minimum when these three quantities are equal.

(7) Find the maximum or minimum of the function

$$u = x + 2xy + y.$$

(8) The post-office regulations state that no parcel is to be of such a size that its length plus its girth exceeds 6 feet. What is the greatest volume that can be sent by post (a) in the case of a package of rectangular cross-section ; (b) in the case of a package of circular cross-section.

(9) Divide π into 3 parts such that the continued product of their sines may be a maximum or minimum.

(10) Find the maximum or minimum of $u = \dfrac{\epsilon^{x+v}}{xy}$.

(11) Find maximum and minimum of

$$u = y + 2x - 2 \log_\epsilon y - \log_\epsilon x.$$

(12) A telpherage bucket of given capacity has the shape of a horizontal isosceles triangular prism with the apex underneath, and the opposite face open. Find its dimensions in order that the least amount of iron sheet may be used in its construction.

CHAPTER XVII

INTEGRATION

THE great secret has already been revealed that this mysterious symbol $\int$, which is after all only a long S, merely means " the sum of ", or " the sum of all such quantities as ". It therefore resembles that other symbol Σ (the Greek *Sigma*), which is also a sign of summation. There is this difference, however, in the practice of mathematical men as to the use of these signs, that while Σ is generally used to indicate the sum of a number of finite quantities, the integral sign $\int$ is generally used to indicate the summing up of a vast number of small quantities of indefinitely minute magnitude, mere elements in fact, that go to make up the total required. Thus $\int dy = y$, and $\int dx = x$.

Any one can understand how the whole of anything can be conceived of as made up of a lot of little bits ; and the smaller the bits the more of them there will be. Thus, a line one inch long may be conceived as made up of 10 pieces, each $\frac{1}{10}$ of an inch long ; or of 100 parts, each part being $\frac{1}{100}$ of an inch long ; or of 1,000,000 parts, each of which is $\frac{1}{1,000,000}$ of an inch long ; or, pushing the thought to the limits of conceivability, it may be regarded as made up of an infinite number of elements each of which is infinitesimally small.

Yes, you will say, but what is the use of thinking of anything that way? Why not think of it straight off, as a whole? The simple reason is that there are a vast number of cases in which one cannot calculate the bigness of the thing as a whole without reckoning up the sum of a lot of small parts. The process of "*integrating*" is to enable us to calculate totals that otherwise we should be unable to estimate directly.

Let us first take one or two simple cases to familiarize ourselves with this notion of summing up a lot of separate parts.

Consider the series :

$$1 + \tfrac{1}{2} + \tfrac{1}{4} + \tfrac{1}{8} + \tfrac{1}{16} + \tfrac{1}{32} + \tfrac{1}{64} + \text{etc.}$$

Here each member of the series is formed by taking half the value of the preceding one. What is the value of the total if we could go on to an infinite number of terms? Every schoolboy knows that the answer is 2. Think of it, if you like, as a line. Begin with one inch ; add a half inch ; add a quarter ; add an eighth ; and so on. If at any point of the operation

Fig. 46.

we stop, there will still be a piece wanting to make up the whole 2 inches ; and the piece wanting will always be the same size as the last piece added. Thus, if after having put together 1, $\tfrac{1}{2}$, and $\tfrac{1}{4}$, we stop, there will be $\tfrac{1}{4}$ wanting. If we go on till we have added $\tfrac{1}{64}$, there will still be $\tfrac{1}{64}$ wanting. The remainder needed will always be equal to the last term added. By an infinite number of operations only should we reach the actual 2 inches. Practically we should reach it when we got to pieces so small that they could not be drawn—that would be after about 10 terms, for the eleventh term is $\tfrac{1}{1024}$. If we want to go so far that not even a Whitworth's measuring machine would detect it, we should merely have to go to about 20 terms. A microscope would not show even the 18th term! So the infinite number of operations is no such dreadful thing after all. The *integral* is simply the whole lot. But, as we shall see, there are cases in which the integral calculus enables us to get at the *exact* total that there would be as the result of an infinite number of operations. In such cases the integral calculus gives us a *rapid* and easy way of getting at a result that would otherwise require an interminable lot of elaborate working out. So we had best lose no time in learning *how to integrate*.

Slopes of Curves, and the Curves themselves

Let us make a little preliminary enquiry about the slopes of curves. For we have seen that differentiating a curve means finding an expression for its slope (or for its slopes at different points). Can we perform the reverse process of reconstructing the whole curve if the slope (or slopes) are prescribed for us ?

Go back to case (2) on p. 71. Here we have the simplest of curves, a sloping line with the equation

$$y = ax + b.$$

Fig. 47.

We know that here b represents the initial height of y when $x = 0$, and that a, which is the same as $\dfrac{dy}{dx}$, is the "slope" of the line. The line has a constant slope. All along it the elementary triangles $\overset{dy}{\underset{dx}{\diagup}}$ have the same proportion between height and base. Suppose we were to take the dx's and dy's of finite magnitude, so that 10 dx's made up one inch, then there would be ten little triangles like

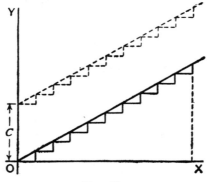

Now, suppose that we were ordered to reconstruct the " curve ", starting merely from the information that $\frac{dy}{dx}=a$. What could we do? Still taking the little d's as of finite size, we could draw 10 of them, all with the same slope, and then put them together, end to end, like this :

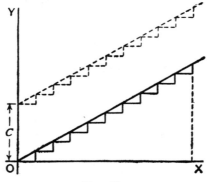

Fig. 48.

And, as the slope is the same for all, they would join to make, as in Fig. 48, a sloping line sloping with the correct slope $\frac{dy}{dx}=a$. And whether we take the dy's and dx's as finite or infinitely small, as they are all alike, clearly $\frac{y}{x}=a$, if we reckon y as the total of all the dy's, and x as the total of all the dx's. But whereabouts are we to put this sloping line? Are we to start at the origin O, or higher up? As the only information we have is as to the slope, we are without any instructions as

F

to the particular height above O ; in fact the initial height is undetermined. The slope will be the same, whatever the initial height. Let us therefore make a shot at what may be wanted, and start the sloping line at a height C above O. That is, we have the equation

$$y = ax + C.$$

It becomes evident now that in this case the added constant means the particular value that y has when $x = 0$.

Now let us take a harder case, that of a line, the slope of which is not constant, but turns up more and more. Let us assume that the upward slope gets greater and greater in proportion as x grows. In symbols this is :

$$\frac{dy}{dx} = ax.$$

Or, to give a concrete case, take $a = \frac{1}{5}$, so that

$$\frac{dy}{dx} = \frac{1}{5}x.$$

Then we had best begin by calculating a few of the values of the slope at different values of x, and also draw little diagrams of them.

When $\qquad x = 0, \quad \dfrac{dy}{dx} = 0,$

$\qquad\qquad x = 1, \quad \dfrac{dy}{dx} = 0.2,$

$\qquad\qquad x = 2, \quad \dfrac{dy}{dx} = 0.4,$

$\qquad\qquad x = 3, \quad \dfrac{dy}{dx} = 0.6,$

$\qquad\qquad x = 4, \quad \dfrac{dy}{dx} = 0.8,$

$\qquad\qquad x = 5, \quad \dfrac{dy}{dx} = 1.0.$

Now try to put the pieces together, setting each so that the middle of its base is the proper distance to the right, and so that they fit together at the corners ; thus (Fig. 49). The result is, of course, not a smooth curve : but it is an approximation to one. If we had taken bits half as long, and twice as numerous, like Fig. 50, we should have a better approximation.

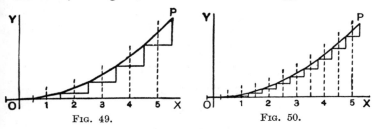

FIG. 49.   FIG. 50.

But for a perfect curve we ought to take each dx and its corresponding dy infinitesimally small, and infinitely numerous.

Then, how much ought the value of any y to be? Clearly, at any point P of the curve, the value of y will be the sum of all the little dy's from 0 up to that level, that is to say, $\int dy = y$. And as each dy is equal to $\frac{1}{5}x \cdot dx$, it follows that the whole y will be equal to the sum of all such bits as $\frac{1}{5}x \cdot dx$, or, as we should write it, $\int \frac{1}{5}x \cdot dx$.

Now if x had been constant, $\int \frac{1}{5}x \cdot dx$ would have been the same as $\frac{1}{5}x \int dx$, or $\frac{1}{5}x^2$. But x began by being 0, and increases to the particular value of x at the point P, so that its average value from 0 to that point is $\frac{1}{2}x$. Hence $\int \frac{1}{5}x \, dx = \frac{1}{10}x^2$; or $y = \frac{1}{10}x^2$.

But, as in the previous case, this requires the addition of an undetermined constant C, because we have not been told at what height above the origin the curve will begin, when $x = 0$. So we write, as the equation of the curve drawn in Fig. 51,

$$y = \tfrac{1}{10}x^2 + C.$$

Fig. 51.

EXERCISES XVI

(See page 247 for Answers)

(1) Find the ultimate sum of $\tfrac{2}{3} + \tfrac{1}{3} + \tfrac{1}{6} + \tfrac{1}{12} + \tfrac{1}{24} + $ etc.

(2) Show that the series $1 - \tfrac{1}{2} + \tfrac{1}{3} - \tfrac{1}{4} + \tfrac{1}{5} - \tfrac{1}{6} + \tfrac{1}{7}$ etc., is convergent, and find its sum to 8 terms.

(3) If $\log_\epsilon (1 + x) = x - \dfrac{x^2}{2} + \dfrac{x^3}{3} - \dfrac{x^4}{4} + $ etc., find $\log_\epsilon 1 \cdot 3$.

(4) Following a reasoning similar to that explained in this chapter, find y,

$$(a) \text{ if } \frac{dy}{dx} = \tfrac{1}{4}x \; ; \quad (b) \text{ if } \frac{dy}{dx} = \cos x.$$

(5) If $\dfrac{dy}{dx} = 2x + 3$, find y.

CHAPTER XVIII

INTEGRATING AS THE REVERSE OF DIFFERENTIATING

DIFFERENTIATING is the process by which when y is given us as a function of x, we can find $\dfrac{dy}{dx}$.

Like every other mathematical operation, the process of differentiation may be reversed. Thus, if differentiating $y = x^4$ gives us $\dfrac{dy}{dx} = 4x^3$, then, if one begins with $\dfrac{dy}{dx} = 4x^3$, one would say that reversing the process would yield $y = x^4$. But here comes in a curious point. We should get $\dfrac{dy}{dx} = 4x^3$ if we had begun with *any* of the following : x^4, or $x^4 + a$, or $x^4 + c$, or x^4 with *any* added constant. So it is clear that in working backwards from $\dfrac{dy}{dx}$ to y, one must make provision for the possibility of there being an added constant, the value of which will be undetermined until ascertained in some other way. So, if differentiating x^n yields nx^{n-1}, going backwards from $\dfrac{dy}{dx} = nx^{n-1}$ will give us $y = x^n + C$; where C stands for the yet undetermined possible constant.

Clearly, in dealing with powers of x, the rule for working backwards will be : Increase the power by 1, then divide by that increased power, and add the undetermined constant.

So, in the case where

$$\frac{dy}{dx} = x^n,$$

159

working backwards, we get

$$y = \frac{1}{n+1} x^{n+1} + C.$$

If differentiating the equation $y = ax^n$ gives us

$$\frac{dy}{dx} = anx^{n-1},$$

it is a matter of common sense that beginning with

$$\frac{dy}{dx} = anx^{n-1},$$

and reversing the process, will give us

$$y = ax^n.$$

So, when we are dealing with a multiplying constant, we must simply put the constant as a multiplier of the result of the integration.

Thus, if $\frac{dy}{dx} = 4x^2$, the reverse process gives us $y = \frac{4}{3}x^3$.

But this is incomplete. For we must remember that if we had started with

$$y = ax^n + C,$$

where C is any constant-quantity whatever, we should equally have found

$$\frac{dy}{dx} = anx^{n-1}.$$

So, therefore, when we reverse the process we must always remember to add on this undetermined constant, even if we do not yet know what its value will be.

This process, the reverse of differentiating, is called *integrating*; for it consists in finding the value of the whole quantity y when you are given only an expression for dy or for $\frac{dy}{dx}$. Hitherto we have as much as possible kept dy and dx together

as a differential coefficient : henceforth we shall more often
have to separate them.

If we begin with a simple case,

$$\frac{dy}{dx} = x^2.$$

We may write this, if we like, as

$$dy = x^2 dx.$$

Now this is a " differential equation " which informs us that
an element of y is equal to the corresponding element of x
multiplied by x^2. Now, what we want is the integral ; therefore, write down with the proper symbol the instructions to
integrate both sides, thus :

$$\int dy = \int x^2 dx.$$

[Note as to reading integrals : the above would be read
thus :

" *Integral dee-wy* equals *integral eks-squared dee-eks.*"]

We haven't yet integrated : we have only written down
instructions to integrate—if we can. Let us try. Plenty of
other fools can do it—why not we also? The left-hand side is
simplicity itself. The sum of all the bits of y is the same
thing as y itself. So we may at once put :

$$y = \int x^2 dx.$$

But when we come to the right-hand side of the equation
we must remember that what we have got to sum up together
is not all the dx's, but all such terms as $x^2 dx$; and this will
not be the same as $x^2 \int dx$, because x^2 is not a constant. For
some of the dx's will be multiplied by big values of x^2, and
some will be multiplied by small values of x^2, according to
what x happens to be. So we must bethink ourselves as to

what we know about this process of integration being the reverse of differentiation. Now, our rule for this reversed process—see p. 159 *ante*—when dealing with x^n is " increase the power by one, and divide by the same number as this increased power ". That is to say, $x^2 dx$ will be changed * to $\frac{1}{3}x^3$. Put this into the equation ; but don't forget to add the " constant of integration " C at the end. So we get :

$$y = \tfrac{1}{3}x^3 + C.$$

You have actually performed the integration. How easy ! Let us try another simple case.

Let $$\frac{dy}{dx} = ax^{12},$$

where a is any constant multiplier. Well, we found when differentiating (see pp. 24–5) that any constant factor in the value of y reappeared unchanged in the value of $\frac{dy}{dx}$. In the reversed process of integrating, it will therefore also reappear in the value of y. So we may go to work as before, thus :

$$dy = ax^{12} \cdot dx,$$
$$\int dy = \int ax^{12} \cdot dx,$$
$$\int dy = a \int x^{12} dx,$$
$$y = a \times \tfrac{1}{13}x^{13} + C.$$

So that is done. How easy !

We begin to realize now that integrating is a process *of finding our way back*, as compared with differentiating. If

* You may ask : what has become of the little dx at the end ? Well, remember that it was really part of the differential coefficient, and when changed over to the right-hand side, as in the $x^2 dx$, serves as a reminder that x is the independent variable with respect to which the operation is to be effected ; and, as the result of the product being totalled up, the power of x has increased by *one*. You will soon become familiar with all this.

ever, during differentiating, we have found any particular
expression—in this example ax^{12}—we can find our way back
to the y from which it was derived. The contrast between
the two processes may be illustrated by the following illustration due to a well-known teacher. If a stranger were set down
in Trafalgar Square, and told to find his way to Euston
Station, he might find the task hopeless. But if he had pre-
viously been personally conducted from Euston Station to
Trafalgar Square, it would be comparatively easy to him to
find his way back to Euston Station.

Integration of the Sum or Difference of two Functions

Let
$$\frac{dy}{dx} = x^2 + x^3,$$

then
$$dy = x^2 dx + x^3 dx.$$

There is no reason why we should not integrate each term
separately ; for, as may be seen on p. 30, we found that when
we differentiated the sum of two separate functions, the differential coefficient was simply the sum of the two separate
differentiations. So, when we work backwards, integrating,
the integration will be simply the sum of the two separate
integrations.

Our instructions will then be :

$$\int dy = \int (x^2 + x^3)\, dx$$
$$= \int x^2 dx + \int x^3 dx$$
$$y = \tfrac{1}{3}x^3 + \tfrac{1}{4}x^4 + C.$$

If either of the terms had been a negative quantity, the
corresponding term in the integral would have also been
negative. So that differences are as readily dealt with as
sums.

How to deal with Constant Terms

Suppose there is in the expression to be integrated a constant term—such as this :

$$\frac{dy}{dx} = x^n + b.$$

This is laughably easy. For you have only to remember that when you differentiated the expression $y = ax$, the result was $\frac{dy}{dx} = a$. Hence, when you work the other way and integrate, the constant reappears multiplied by x. So we get

$$dy = x^n dx + b \cdot dx,$$

$$\int dy = \int x^n dx + \int b\, dx.$$

$$y = \frac{1}{n+1} x^{n+1} + bx + C.$$

Here are a lot of examples on which to try your newly acquired powers.

Examples.

(1) Given $\frac{dy}{dx} = 24x^{11}$. Find y.   *Ans.* $y = 2x^{12} + C$.

(2) Find $\int (a+b)(x+1)\, dx$. It is $(a+b)\int (x+1)\, dx$

or $(a+b)\left[\int x\, dx + \int dx\right]$ or $(a+b)\left(\frac{x^2}{2} + x\right) + C$.

(3) Given $\frac{du}{dt} = gt^{\frac{1}{2}}$. Find u.   *Ans.* $u = \frac{2}{3} gt^{\frac{3}{2}} + C$.

(4) $\frac{dy}{dx} = x^3 - x^2 + x$.   Find y.

$$dy = (x^3 - x^2 + x)\, dx$$

or $dy = x^3 dx - x^2 dx + x\, dx$; $y = \int x^3 dx - \int x^2 dx + \int x\, dx$;

and $y = \frac{1}{4}x^4 - \frac{1}{3}x^3 + \frac{1}{2}x^2 + C$.

(5) Integrate $9 \cdot 75 x^{2 \cdot 25} dx$.   *Ans.* $y = 3x^{3 \cdot 25} + C$.

All these are easy enough.   Let us try another case.

Let $\dfrac{dy}{dx} = ax^{-1}.$

Proceeding as before, we will write

$$dy = ax^{-1} \cdot dx, \quad \int dy = a \int x^{-1} dx.$$

Well, but what is the integral of $x^{-1} dx$?

If you look back amongst the results of differentiating x^2 and x^3 and x^n, etc., you will find we never got x^{-1} from any one of them as the value of $\dfrac{dy}{dx}$.   We got $3x^2$ from x^3 ; we got $2x$ from x^2 ; we got 1 from x^1 (that is, from x itself) ; but we did not get x^{-1} from x^0, for two very good reasons.   *First*, x^0 is simply $=1$, and is a constant, and could not have a differential coefficient.   *Secondly*, even if it could be differentiated, its differential coefficient (got by slavishly following the usual rule) would be $0 \times x^{-1}$, and that multiplication by zero gives it zero value!   Therefore when we now come to try to integrate $x^{-1} dx$, we see that it does not come in anywhere in the powers of x that are given by the rule :

$$\int x^n dx = \frac{1}{n+1} x^{n+1}.$$

It is an exceptional case.

Well ; but try again.   Look through all the various differentials obtained from various functions of x, and try to find amongst them x^{-1}.   A sufficient search will show that we actually did get $\dfrac{dy}{dx} = x^{-1}$ as the result of differentiating the function $y = \log_\epsilon x$ (see p. 123).

Then, of course, since we know that differentiating $\log_\epsilon x$ gives us x^{-1}, we know that, by reversing the process, integrating $dy = x^{-1}dx$ will give us $y = \log_\epsilon x$. But we must not forget the constant factor a that was given, nor must we omit to add the undetermined constant of integration. This then gives us as the solution to the present problem,

$$y = a \log_\epsilon x + C.$$

N.B.—Here note this very remarkable fact, that we could not have integrated in the above case if we had not happened to know the corresponding differentiation. If no one had found out that differentiating $\log_\epsilon x$ gave x^{-1}, we should have been utterly stuck by the problem how to integrate $x^{-1}dx$. Indeed it should be frankly admitted that this is one of the curious features of the integral calculus :—that you can't integrate anything before the reverse process of differentiating something else has yielded that expression which you want to integrate. No one, even to-day, is able to find the general integral of the expression,

$$\frac{dy}{dx} = a^{-x^2},$$

because a^{-x^2} has never yet been found to result from differentiating anything else.

Another simple case.

Find $\int (x+1)(x+2) dx$.

On looking at the function to be integrated, you remark that it is the product of two different functions of x. You could, you think, integrate $(x+1) dx$ by itself, or $(x+2) dx$ by itself. Of course you could. But what to do with a product? None of the differentiations you have learned have yielded you for the differential coefficient a product like this. Failing such, the simplest thing is to multiply up the two functions, and then integrate. This gives us

$$\int (x^2 + 3x + 2)\, dx.$$

And this is the same as

$$\int x^2\, dx + \int 3x\, dx + \int 2\, dx.$$

And performing the integrations, we get

$$\tfrac{1}{3}x^3 + \tfrac{3}{2}x^2 + 2x + C.$$

Some other Integrals

Now that we know that integration is the reverse of differentiation, we may at once look up the differential coefficients we already know, and see from what functions they were derived. This gives us the following integrals ready made :

x^{-1} (pp. 122–3) ; $\displaystyle\int x^{-1}\, dx = \log_\epsilon x + C.$

$\displaystyle\frac{1}{x+a}$ (p. 123) ; $\displaystyle\int \frac{1}{x+a}\, dx = \log_\epsilon (x+a) + C.$

ϵ^x (p. 118) ; $\displaystyle\int \epsilon^x\, dx = \epsilon^x + C.$

ϵ^{-x} $\displaystyle\int \epsilon^{-x}\, dx = -\epsilon^{-x} + C$

(for if $y = -\dfrac{1}{\epsilon^x}$, $\dfrac{dy}{dx} = -\dfrac{\epsilon^x \times 0 - 1 \times \epsilon^x}{\epsilon^{2x}} = \epsilon^{-x}$).

$\sin x$ (pp. 137–8) ; $\displaystyle\int \sin x\, dx = -\cos x + C.$

$\cos x$ (p. 139) ; $\displaystyle\int \cos x\, dx = \sin x + C.$

Also we may deduce the following :

$$\log_\epsilon x \; ; \qquad \int \log_\epsilon x \, dx = x(\log_\epsilon x - 1) + C$$

(for if $y = x \log_\epsilon x - x$, $\dfrac{dy}{dx} = \dfrac{x}{x} + \log_\epsilon x - 1 = \log_\epsilon x$).

$$\log_{10} x \; ; \qquad \int \log_{10} x \, dx = 0 \cdot 4343 x \, (\log_\epsilon x - 1) + C.$$

$$a^x \quad \text{(p. 124)} \; ; \qquad \int a^x \, dx \quad = \dfrac{a^x}{\log_\epsilon a} + C.$$

$$\cos ax \; ; \qquad \int \cos ax \, dx = \dfrac{1}{a} \sin ax + C$$

(for if $y = \sin ax$, $\dfrac{dy}{dx} = a \cos ax$; hence to get $\cos ax$ one **must** differentiate $y = \dfrac{1}{a} \sin ax$)

$$\sin ax \; ; \qquad \int \sin ax \, dx = - \dfrac{1}{a} \cos ax + C.$$

Try also $\cos^2 \theta$; a little dodge will simplify matters :

$$\cos 2\theta = \cos^2 \theta - \sin^2 \theta = 2 \cos^2 \theta - 1 \; ;$$

hence $\qquad\qquad \cos^2 \theta = \tfrac{1}{2} (\cos 2\theta + 1),$

and $\qquad\qquad \displaystyle\int \cos^2 \theta \, d\theta = \tfrac{1}{2} \int (\cos 2\theta + 1) \, d\theta$

$$= \tfrac{1}{2} \int \cos 2\theta \, d\theta + \tfrac{1}{2} \int d\theta$$

$$= \dfrac{\sin 2\theta}{4} + \dfrac{\theta}{2} + C. \quad \text{(See also p. 189.)}$$

See also the Table of Standard Forms on pp. 238–9. You should make such a table for yourself, putting in it only the general functions which you have successfully differentiated and integrated. See to it that it grows steadily!

On Double and Triple Integrals

In many cases it is necessary to integrate some expression
for two or more variables contained in it ; and in that case
the sign of integration appears more than once. Thus,

$$\iint f(x,\,y)\,dx\,dy$$

means that some function of the variables x and y has to be
integrated for each. It does not matter in which order they
are done. Thus, take the function $x^2 + y^2$. Integrating it with
respect to x gives us :

$$\int (x^2 + y^2)\,dx = \tfrac{1}{3}x^3 + xy^2.$$

Now, integrate this with respect to y :

$$\int (\tfrac{1}{3}x^3 + xy^2)\,dy = \tfrac{1}{3}x^3 y + \tfrac{1}{3}xy^3,$$

to which of course a constant is to be added. If we had
reversed the order of the operations, the result would have
been the same.

In dealing with areas of surfaces and of solids, we have
often to integrate both for length and breadth, and thus have
integrals of the form

$$\iint u \cdot dx\,dy,$$

where u is some property that depends, at each point, on x
and on y. This would then be called a *surface-integral*. It
indicates that the value of all such elements as $u \cdot dx \cdot dy$ (that
is to say, of the value of u over a little rectangle dx long and
dy broad) has to be summed up over the whole length and
whole breadth.

Similarly in the case of solids, where we deal with three
dimensions. Consider any element of volume, the small cube

whose dimensions are $dx\,dy\,dz$. If the figure of the solid be expressed by the function $f(x, y, z)$, then the whole solid will have the *volume-integral*,

$$\text{volume} = \iiint f(x, y, z) \cdot dx \cdot dy \cdot dz.$$

Naturally, such integrations have to be taken between appropriate limits * in each dimension ; and the integration cannot be performed unless one knows in what way the boundaries of the surface depend on x, y, and z. If the limits for x are from x_1 to x_2, those for y from y_1 to y_2, and those for z from z_1 to z_2, then clearly we have

$$\text{volume} = \int_{z_1}^{z_2}\int_{y_1}^{y_2}\int_{x_1}^{x_2} f(x, y, z) \cdot dx \cdot dy \cdot dz.$$

There are of course plenty of complicated and difficult cases ; but, in general, it is quite easy to see the significance of the symbols where they are intended to indicate that a certain integration has to be performed over a given surface, or throughout a given solid space.

EXERCISES XVII

(See page 247 for Answers)

(1) Find $\int y\,dx$ when $y^2 = 4ax$.

(2) Find $\int \dfrac{3}{x^4}\,dx.$

(3) Find $\int \dfrac{1}{a}\,x^3\,dx.$

(4) Find $\int (x^2 + a)\,dx.$

(5) Integrate $5x^{-\frac{7}{2}}.$

(6) Find $\int (4x^3 + 3x^2 + 2x + 1)\,dx.$

* See pp. 173-4 for integration between limits.

(7) If $\dfrac{dy}{dx} = \dfrac{ax}{2} + \dfrac{bx^2}{3} + \dfrac{cx^3}{4}$; find y.

(8) Find $\displaystyle\int \left(\dfrac{x^2 + a}{x + a}\right) dx.$ (9) Find $\displaystyle\int (x+3)^3 dx.$

(10) Find $\displaystyle\int (x+2)(x-a)\,dx.$

(11) Find $\displaystyle\int (\sqrt{x} + \sqrt[3]{x})\, 3a^2\, dx.$

(12) Find $\displaystyle\int (\sin \theta - \tfrac{1}{2}) \dfrac{d\theta}{3}.$

(13) Find $\displaystyle\int \cos^2 a\theta\, d\theta.$ (14) Find $\displaystyle\int \sin^2 \theta\, d\theta.$

(15) Find $\displaystyle\int \sin^2 a\theta\, d\theta.$ (16) Find $\displaystyle\int \epsilon^{3x}\, dx.$

(17) Find $\displaystyle\int \dfrac{dx}{1 + x}.$ (18) Find $\displaystyle\int \dfrac{dx}{1 - x}.$

CHAPTER XIX

ON FINDING AREAS BY INTEGRATING

ONE use of the integral calculus is to enable us to ascertain the values of areas bounded by curves.

Let us try to get at the subject bit by bit.

Let *AB* (Fig. 52) be a curve, the equation to which is known. That is, *y* in this curve is some known function of *x*.

FIG. 52.

Think of a piece of the curve from the point *P* to the point *Q*.

Let a perpendicular *PM* be dropped from *P*, and another *QN* from the point *Q*. Then call $OM = x_1$ and $ON = x_2$, and the ordinates $PM = y_1$ and $QN = y_2$. We have thus marked out the area *PQNM* that lies beneath the piece *PQ*. The problem is, *how can we calculate the value of this area?*

The secret of solving this problem is to conceive the area as being divided up into a lot of narrow strips, each of them being of the width *dx*. The smaller we take *dx*, the more of them there will be between x_1 and x_2. Now, the whole area is clearly equal to the sum of the areas of all such strips. Our business will then be to discover an expression for the area of any one narrow strip, and to integrate it so as to add together all the

strips.   Now think of any one of the strips.   It will be like this :
being bounded between two vertical sides, with a flat bottom
dx, and with a slightly curved sloping top.   Suppose we
take its *average* height as being y ;   then, as its width is
dx, its area will be $y\,dx$.   And seeing that we may take
the width as narrow as we please, if we only take it
narrow enough its average height will be the same as
the height at the middle of it.   Now let us call the unknown value of the whole area S, meaning surface.
The area of one strip will be simply a bit of the
whole area, and may therefore be called dS.   So we may
write

$$\text{area of 1 strip} = dS = y \cdot dx.$$

If then we add up all the strips, we get

$$\text{total area } S = \int dS = \int y\,dx.$$

So then our finding S depends on whether we can integrate
$y \cdot dx$ for the particular case, when we know what the value of
y is as a function of x.

For instance, if you were told that for the particular curve
in question $y = b + ax^2$, no doubt you could put that value into
the expression and say : then I must find $\int (b + ax^2)\,dx$.

That is all very well ;   but a little thought will show you
that something more must be done.   Because the area we are
trying to find is not the area under the whole length of the
curve, but only the area limited on the left by PM, and on
the right by QN, it follows that we must do something to
define our area between those "*limits*".

This introduces us to a new notion, namely, that of *integrating between limits*.   We suppose x to vary, and for the present
purpose we do not require any value of x below x_1 (that is
OM), nor any value of x above x_2 (that is ON).   When an

integral is to be thus defined between two limits, we call the lower of the two values *the inferior limit*, and the upper value *the superior limit*. Any integral so limited we designate as a *definite integral*, by way of distinguishing it from a *general integral* to which no limits are assigned.

In the symbols which give instructions to integrate, the limits are marked by putting them at the top and bottom respectively of the sign of integration. Thus the instruction

$$\int_{x=x_1}^{x=x_2} y \cdot dx$$

will be read : find the integral of $y \cdot dx$ between the inferior limit x_1 and the superior limit x_2.

Sometimes the thing is written more simply

$$\int_{x_1}^{x_2} y \cdot dx.$$

Well, but *how* do you find an integral between limits, when you have got these instructions?

Look again at Fig. 52 (p. 172). Suppose we could find the area under the larger piece of curve from A to Q, that is from $x=0$ to $x=x_2$, naming the area $AQNO$. Then, suppose we could find the area under the smaller piece from A to P, that is from $x=0$ to $x=x_1$, namely, the area $APMO$. If then we were to subtract the smaller area from the larger, we should have left as a remainder the area $PQNM$, which is what we want. Here we have the clue as to what to do ; the definite integral between the two limits is *the difference* between the integral worked out for the superior limit and the integral worked out for the lower limit.

Let us then go ahead. First, find the general integral thus :

$$\int y \, dx,$$

and, as $y = b + ax^2$ is the equation to the curve (Fig. 52),

$$\int (b + ax^2)\, dx$$

is the general integral which we must find.

Doing the integration in question by the rule (p. 163), we get

$$bx + \frac{a}{3}\, x^3 + C \; ;$$

and this will be the whole area from 0 up to any value of x that we may assign.

Therefore, the larger area up to the superior limit x_2 will be

$$bx_2 + \frac{a}{3}\, x_2{}^3 + C \; ;$$

and the smaller area up to the inferior limit x_1 will be

$$bx_1 + \frac{a}{3}\, x_1{}^3 + C.$$

Now, subtract the smaller from the larger, and we get **for** the area S the value,

$$\text{area } S = b\, (x_2 - x_1) + \frac{a}{3}(x_2{}^3 - x_1{}^3).$$

This is the answer we wanted. Let us give some numerical values. Suppose $b = 10$, $a = 0 \cdot 06$, and $x_2 = 8$ and $x_1 = 6$. Then the area S is equal to

$$10\,(8 - 6) + \frac{0 \cdot 06}{3}(8^3 - 6^3)$$
$$= 20 + 0 \cdot 02\,(512 - 216)$$
$$= 20 + 0 \cdot 02 \times 296$$
$$= 20 + 5 \cdot 92$$
$$= 25 \cdot 92.$$

Let us here put down a symbolic way of stating what **we** have ascertained about limits :

$$\int_{x = x_1}^{x = x_2} y\, dx = y_2 - y_1,$$

where y_2 is the integrated value of $y\,dx$ corresponding to x_2, and y_1 that corresponding to x_1.

All integration between limits requires the difference between two values to be thus found. Also note that, in making the subtraction the added constant C has disappeared.

Examples.

(1) To familiarize ourselves with the process, let us take a case of which we know the answer beforehand. Let us find the area of the triangle (Fig. 53), which has base $x = 12$ and

Fig. 53.

height $y = 4$. We know beforehand, from obvious mensuration, that the answer will come to 24.

Now, here we have as the " curve " a sloping line for which the equation is

$$y = \frac{x}{3}.$$

The area in question will be

$$\int_{x=0}^{x=12} y \cdot dx = \int_{x=0}^{x=12} \frac{x}{3} \cdot dx.$$

Integrating $\frac{x}{3}\,dx$ (p. 162), and putting down the value of the general integral in square brackets with the limits marked above and below, we get

$$\text{area} = \left[\frac{1}{3} \cdot \frac{1}{2} x^2 + C\right]_{x=0}^{x=12}$$
$$= \left[\frac{x^2}{6} + C\right]_{x=0}^{x=12}$$

$$\text{area} = \left[\frac{12^2}{6} + C\right] - \left[\frac{0^2}{6} + C\right]$$

$$= \frac{144}{6} = 24.$$

Note that, in dealing with definite integrals, the constant C always disappears by subtraction.

FIG. 54.

Let us satisfy ourselves about this rather surprising dodge of calculation, by testing it on a simple example. Get some squared paper, preferably some that is ruled in little squares of one-eighth or one-tenth inch each way. On this squared paper plot out the graph of this equation,

$$y = \frac{x}{3}.$$

The values to be plotted will be :

x	0	3	6	9	12
y	0	1	2	3	4

The plot is given in Fig. 54.

Now reckon out the area beneath the curve *by counting the little squares* below the line, from $x = 0$ as far as $x = 12$ on the right. There are 18 whole squares and four triangles, each of which has an area equal to $1\frac{1}{2}$ squares ; or, in total, 24 squares.

Hence 24 is the numerical value of the integral of $\frac{x}{3}\,dx$ between the lower limit of $x = 0$ and the higher limit of $x = 12$.

As a further exercise, show that the value of the same integral between the limits of $x = 3$ and $x = 15$ is 36.

(2) Find the area, between limits $x = x_1$ and $x = 0$, of the curve $y = \dfrac{b}{x+a}$.

Fig. 55.

$$\text{Area} = \int_{x=0}^{x=x_1} y \cdot dx = \int_{x=0}^{x=x_1} \frac{b}{x+a}\, dx$$
$$= b \left[\log_\epsilon (x+a) + C \right]_0^{x_1}$$
$$= b [\log_\epsilon (x_1 + a) + C - \log_\epsilon (0+a) - C]$$
$$= b \log_\epsilon \frac{x_1 + a}{a}.$$

Let it be noted that this process of subtracting one part from a larger to find the difference is really a common practice. How do you find the area of a plane ring (Fig. 56), the outer

Fig. 56.

radius of which is r_2 and the inner radius is r_1? You know
from mensuration that the area of the outer circle is $\pi r_2{}^2$;
then you find the area of the inner circle, $\pi r_1{}^2$; then you
subtract the latter from the former, and find area of ring
$= \pi(r_2{}^2 - r_1{}^2)$; which may be written

$$\pi(r_2 + r_1)(r_2 - r_1)$$

= mean circumference of ring × width of ring.

(3) Here's another case—that of *the die-away curve* (p. 129).
Find the area between $x = 0$ and $x = a$ of the curve (Fig. 57)
whose equation is

$$y = b\epsilon^{-x}.$$
$$\text{Area} = b \int_{x=0}^{x=a} \epsilon^{-x} \cdot dx.$$

The integration (p. 167) gives

$$= b\left[-\epsilon^{-x} \right]_0^a$$
$$= b\left[-\epsilon^{-a} - (-\epsilon^{-0}) \right]$$
$$= b(1 - \epsilon^{-a}).$$

Fig. 57.

Fig. 58.

(4) Another example is afforded by the adiabatic curve of
a perfect gas, the equation to which is $pv^n = c$, where p stands
for pressure, v for volume, and n has the value $1 \cdot 42$ (Fig. 58).
Find the area under the curve (which is Proportional to the

work done in suddenly compressing the gas) from volume v_2 to volume v_1.

Here we have

$$\text{area} = \int_{v=v_1}^{v=v_2} cv^{-n} \cdot dv$$

$$= c\left[\frac{1}{1-n} v^{1-n}\right]_{v_1}^{v_2}$$

$$= c\,\frac{1}{1-n}(v_2{}^{1-n} - v_1{}^{1-n})$$

$$= \frac{-c}{0\cdot42}\left(\frac{1}{v_2{}^{0\cdot42}} - \frac{1}{v_1{}^{0\cdot42}}\right).$$

An Exercise.

Prove the ordinary mensuration formula, that the area A of a circle whose radius is R, is equal to πR^2.

Consider an elementary zone or annulus of the surface (Fig. 59), of breadth dr, situated at a distance r from the centre.

FIG. 59.

We may consider the entire surface as consisting of such narrow zones, and the whole area A will simply be the integral of all such elementary zones from centre to margin, that is, integrated from $r = 0$ to $r = R$.

We have therefore to find an expression for the elementary area dA of the narrow zone. Think of it as a strip of breadth dr, and of a length that is the periphery of the circle of radius

r, that is, a length of $2\pi r$. Then we have, as the area of the narrow zone, $dA = 2\pi r\, dr$.

Hence the area of the whole circle will be :

$$A = \int dA = \int_{r=0}^{r=R} 2\pi r \cdot dr = 2\pi \int_{r=0}^{r=R} r \cdot dr.$$

Now, the general integral of $r \cdot dr$ is $\frac{1}{2}r^2$. Therefore,

$$A = 2\pi \left[\tfrac{1}{2}r^2 \right]_{r=0}^{r=R};$$

or

$$A = 2\pi [\tfrac{1}{2}R^2 - \tfrac{1}{2}(0)^2];$$

whence

$$A = \pi R^2.$$

Another Exercise.

Let us find the mean ordinate of the positive part of the curve $y = x - x^2$, which is shown in Fig. 60. To find the mean

Fɪɢ. 60.

ordinate, we shall have to find the area of the piece OMN, and then divide it by the length of the base ON. But before we can find the area we must ascertain the length of the base, so as to know up to what limit we are to integrate. At N the ordinate y has zero value ; therefore, we must look at the equation and see what value of x will make $y = 0$. Now, clearly, if x is 0, y will also be 0, the curve passing through the origin O ; but also, if $x = 1$, $y = 0$: so that $x = 1$ gives us the position of the point N.

Then the area wanted is

$$= \int_{x=0}^{x=1} (x - x^2)\, dx = \left[\tfrac{1}{2}x^2 - \tfrac{1}{3}x^3 \right]_0^1 = [\tfrac{1}{2} - \tfrac{1}{3}] - [0 - 0] = \tfrac{1}{6}.$$

But the base length is 1.

Therefore, the average ordinate of the curve $= \frac{1}{8}$.

[*N.B.*—It will be a pretty and simple exercise in maxima and minima to find by differentiation what is the height of the maximum ordinate. It *must* be greater than the average.]

The mean ordinate of any curve, over a range from $x = 0$ to $x = x_1$, is given by the expression,

$$\text{mean } y = \frac{1}{x_1} \int_{x=0}^{x=x_1} y \cdot dx.$$

If the mean ordinate be required over a distance not beginning at the origin but beginning at a point distant x_1 from the origin and ending at a point distant x_2 from the origin, the value will be

$$\text{mean } y = \frac{1}{x_2 - x_1} \int_{x=x_1}^{x=x_2} y \, dx.$$

Areas in Polar Coordinates

When the equation of the boundary of an area is given as a function of the distance r of a point of it from a fixed point O (see Fig. 61) called the *pole*, and of the angle which r makes

Fig. 61.

with the positive horizontal direction OX, the process just explained can be applied just as easily, with a small modification. Instead of a strip of area, we consider a small triangle OAB, the angle at O being $d\theta$, and we find the sum of all the little triangles making up the required area.

The area of such a small triangle is approximately $\dfrac{AB}{2} \times r$ or $\dfrac{r\,d\theta}{2} \times r$; hence the portion of the area included between the curve and two positions of r corresponding to the angles θ_1 and θ_2 is given by

$$\tfrac{1}{2}\int_{\theta=\theta_1}^{\theta=\theta_2} r^2\,d\theta.$$

Examples.

(1) Find the area of the sector of 1 radian in a circumference of radius a inch.

The polar equation of the circumference is evidently $r = a$. The area is

$$\tfrac{1}{2}\int_{\theta=0}^{\theta=1} a^2\,d\theta = \frac{a^2}{2}\int_{\theta=0}^{\theta=1} d\theta = \frac{a^2}{2}\,.$$

(2) Find the area of the first quadrant of the curve (known as " Pascal's Snail "), the polar equation of which is

$$r = a(1 + \cos\,\theta).$$

$$\begin{aligned}
\text{Area} &= \tfrac{1}{2}\int_{\theta=0}^{\theta=\frac{\pi}{2}} a^2(1 + \cos\,\theta)^2\,d\theta \\
&= \frac{a^2}{2}\int_{\theta=0}^{\theta=\frac{\pi}{2}}(1 + 2\,\cos\,\theta + \cos^2\,\theta)\,d\theta \\
&= \frac{a^2}{2}\left[\theta + 2\,\sin\,\theta + \frac{\theta}{2} + \frac{\sin\,2\theta}{4}\right]_0^{\frac{\pi}{2}} \quad \text{(see p. 168)} \\
&= \frac{a^2(3\pi + 8)}{8}\,.
\end{aligned}$$

Volumes by Integration

What we have done with the area of a little strip of a surface, we can, of course, just as easily do with the volume of a little strip of a solid. We can add up all the little strips that make up the total solid, and find its volume, just as we have added up all the small little bits that made up an area to find the final area of the figure operated upon.

Examples.

(1) Find the volume of a sphere of radius *r*.

A thin spherical shell has for volume $4\pi x^2\,dx$ (see Fig. 59, p. 180); summing up all the concentric shells which make up the sphere, we have

$$\text{volume sphere} = \int_{x=0}^{x=r} 4\pi x^2\,dx = 4\pi\left[\frac{x^3}{3}\right]_0^r = \tfrac{4}{3}\pi r^3.$$

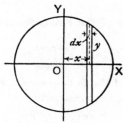

FIG. 62.

We can also proceed as follows : a slice of the sphere, of thickness *dx*, has for volume $\pi y^2\,dx$ (see Fig. 62). Also *x* and *y* are related by the expression

$$y^2 = r^2 - x^2.$$

Hence
$$\begin{aligned}
\text{volume sphere} &= 2\int_{x=0}^{x=r} \pi(r^2 - x^2)\,dx \\
&= 2\pi\left[\int_{x=0}^{x=r} r^2\,dx - \int_{x=0}^{x=r} x^2\,dx\right] \\
&= 2\pi\left[r^2 x - \frac{x^3}{3}\right]_0^r = \frac{4\pi}{3}r^3.
\end{aligned}$$

(2) Find the volume of the solid generated by the revolution of the curve $y^2 = 6x$ about the axis of *x*, between $x = 0$ and $x = 4$.

The volume of a slice of the solid is $\pi y^2 dx$.

Hence
$$\text{volume} = \int_{x=0}^{x=4} \pi y^2 dx = 6\pi \int_{x=0}^{x=4} x\,dx$$
$$= 6\pi \left[\frac{x^2}{2} \right]_0^4 = 48\pi = 150 \cdot 8.$$

On Quadratic Means

In certain branches of physics, particularly in the study of alternating electric currents, it is necessary to be able to calculate the *quadratic mean* of a variable quantity. By " quadratic mean " is denoted the square root of the mean of the squares of all the values between the limits considered. Other names for the quadratic mean of any quantity are its " virtual " value, or its " R.M.S. " (meaning root-mean-square) value. The French term is *valeur efficace*. If y is the function under consideration, and the quadratic mean is to be taken between the limits of $x = 0$ and $x = l$; then the quadratic mean is expressed as

$$\sqrt[2]{\frac{1}{l} \int_0^l y^2 dx}.$$

Examples.

(1) To find the quadratic mean of the function $y = ax$ (Fig. 63).

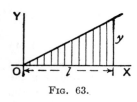

FIG. 63.

Here the integral is $\int_0^l a^2 x^2 dx$, which is $\frac{1}{3} a^2 l^3$. Dividing by l and taking the square root, we have

quadratic mean $= \dfrac{1}{\sqrt{3}} al$.

Here the arithmetical mean is $\frac{1}{2}al$; and the ratio of quadratic to arithmetical mean (this ratio is called the *form-factor*) is $2/\sqrt{3} = 2\sqrt{3}/3 = 1 \cdot 155$.

(2) To find the quadratic mean of the function $y = x^a$.

The integral is $\int_{x=0}^{x=l} x^{2a}\,dx$, that is $\dfrac{l^{2a+1}}{2a+1}$.

Hence $\qquad$ quadratic mean $= \sqrt[2]{\dfrac{l^{2a}}{2a+1}}$.

(3) To find the quadratic mean of the function $y = a^{\frac{x}{2}}$.

The integral is $\int_{x=0}^{x=l} \left(a^{\frac{x}{2}}\right)^2 dx$, that is $\int_{x=0}^{x=l} a^x\,dx$,

or $\qquad \left[\dfrac{a^x}{\log_\epsilon a}\right]_{x=0}^{x=l}$, which is $\dfrac{a^l - 1}{\log_\epsilon a}$.

Hence the quadratic mean is $\sqrt[2]{\dfrac{a^l - 1}{l \log_\epsilon a}}$.

EXERCISES XVIII

(*See page 247 for Answers*)

(1) Find the area of the curve $y = x^2 + x - 5$ between $x = 0$ and $x = 6$, and the mean ordinate between these limits.

(2) Find the area of the parabola $y = 2a\sqrt{x}$ between $x = 0$ and $x = a$. Show that it is two-thirds of the rectangle of the limiting ordinate and of its abscissa.

(3) Find the area of the positive portion of a sine curve and the mean ordinate.

(4) Find the area of the portion of the curve $y = \sin^2 x$ from $0°$ to $180°$, and find the mean ordinate.

(5) Find the area included between the two branches of the curve $y = x^2 \pm x^{\frac{5}{2}}$ from $x = 0$ to $x = 1$, also the area of the positive portion of the lower branch of the curve (see Fig. 30, p. 90).

(6) Find the volume of a cone of radius of base r, and of height h.

(7) Find the area of the curve $y = x^3 - \log_\epsilon x$ between $x = 0$ and $x = 1$.

(8) Find the volume generated by the curve $y = \sqrt{1 + x^2}$, as it revolves about the axis of x, between $x = 0$ and $x = 4$.

(9) Find the volume generated by a sine curve revolving about the axis of x.

(10) Find the area of the portion of the curve $xy = a$ included between $x = 1$ and $x = a$. Find the mean ordinate between these limits.

(11) Show that the quadratic mean of the function $y = \sin x$, between the limits of 0 and π radians, is $\dfrac{\sqrt{2}}{2}$. Find also the arithmetical mean of the same function between the same limits ; and show that the form-factor is $= 1 \cdot 11$.

(12) Find the arithmetical and quadratic means of the function $x^2 + 3x + 2$, from $x = 0$ to $x = 3$.

(13) Find the quadratic mean and the arithmetical mean of the function $y = A_1 \sin x + A_3 \sin 3x$.

(14) A certain curve has the equation $y = 3 \cdot 42 \epsilon^{0 \cdot 21x}$. Find the area included between the curve and the axis of x, from the ordinate at $x = 2$ to the ordinate at $x = 8$. Find also the height of the mean ordinate of the curve between these points.

(15) The curve whose polar equation is $r = a(1 - \cos \theta)$ is known as the cardioid. Show that the area enclosed by the axis and the curve between $\theta = 0$ and $\theta = 2\pi$ radians is equal to $1 \cdot 5$ times that of the circle whose radius is a.

(16) Find the volume generated by the curve

$$y = \pm \frac{x}{6} \sqrt{x(10 - x)}$$

rotating about the axis of x.

CHAPTER XX

DODGES, PITFALLS, AND TRIUMPHS

Dodges. A great part of the labour of integrating things consists in licking them into some shape that can be integrated. The books—and by this is meant the serious books—on the Integral Calculus are full of plans and methods and dodges and artifices for this kind of work. The following are a few of them.

Integration by Parts. This name is given to a dodge, the formula for which is

$$\int u\, dx = ux - \int x\, du + C.$$

It is useful in some cases that you can't tackle directly, for it shows that if in any case $\int x\, du$ can be found, then $\int u\, dx$ can also be found. The formula can be deduced as follows. From p. 32, we have,

$$d(ux) = u\, dx + x\, du,$$

which may be written

$$u\, dx = d(ux) - x\, du,$$

which by direct integration gives the above expression.

Examples.

(1) Find $\int w \cdot \sin w\, dw.$

Write $u = w$, and dx for $\sin w \cdot dw$. We shall then have $du = dw$, while $x = \int \sin w \cdot dw = -\cos w.$

Putting these into the formula, we get

$$\int w \cdot \sin w \, dw = w(-\cos w) - \int -\cos w \, dw$$

$$= -w \cos w + \sin w + C.$$

(2) Find $\int x\epsilon^x dx$.

Write $\qquad u = x, \quad dv = \epsilon^x dx$

then $\qquad du = dx, \quad v = \epsilon^x,$

and $\qquad \int x\epsilon^x dx = x\epsilon^x - \int \epsilon^x dx$ (by the formula)

$$= x\epsilon^x - \epsilon^x + C = \epsilon^x(x-1) + C.$$

(3) Try $\int \cos^2 \theta \, d\theta$.

$$u = \cos \theta, \qquad dx = \cos \theta \, d\theta.$$

Hence $\qquad du = -\sin \theta \, d\theta, \quad x = \sin \theta,$

$$\int \cos^2 \theta \, d\theta = \cos \theta \sin \theta + \int \sin^2 \theta \, d\theta$$

$$= \frac{2 \cos \theta \sin \theta}{2} + \int (1 - \cos^2 \theta) \, d\theta$$

$$= \frac{\sin 2\theta}{2} + \int d\theta - \int \cos^2 \theta \, d\theta.$$

Hence $\qquad 2\int \cos^2 \theta \, d\theta = \frac{\sin 2\theta}{2} + \theta$

and $\qquad \int \cos^2 \theta \, d\theta = \frac{\sin 2\theta}{4} + \frac{\theta}{2} + C.$

(4) Find $\int x^2 \sin x \, dx$.

Write $\qquad u = x^2, \qquad dv = \sin x \, dx ;$

then $\qquad du = 2x \, dx, \quad v = -\cos x,$

$$\int x^2 \sin x \, dx = -x^2 \cos x + 2\int x \cos x \, dx.$$

Now find $\int x \cos x \, dx$, integrating by parts (as in **Example 1** above) :

$$\int x \cos x \, dx = x \sin x + \cos x + C.$$

Hence $\qquad \int x^2 \sin x \, dx = -x^2 \cos x + 2x \sin x + 2 \cos x + C'$

$$= (2 - x^2) \cos x + 2x \sin x + C'.$$

(5) Find $\int \sqrt{1 - x^2} \, dx$.

Write $\qquad\qquad u = \sqrt{1 - x^2}, \quad dx = dv \, ;$

then $\qquad\qquad du = -\dfrac{x \, dx}{\sqrt{1 - x^2}}$ (see Chap. IX, p. 57)

and $x = v$; so that

$$\int \sqrt{1 - x^2} \, dx = x \sqrt{1 - x^2} + \int \frac{x^2 dx}{\sqrt{1 - x^2}} \, .$$

Here we may use a little dodge, for we can write

$$\int \sqrt{1 - x^2} \, dx = \int \frac{(1 - x^2) \, dx}{\sqrt{1 - x^2}} = \int \frac{dx}{\sqrt{1 - x^2}} - \int \frac{x^2 dx}{\sqrt{1 - x^2}} \, .$$

Adding these two last equations, we get rid of $\int \dfrac{x^2 dx}{\sqrt{1 - x^2}}$, and we have

$$2 \int \sqrt{1 - x^2} \, dx = x \sqrt{1 - x^2} + \int \frac{dx}{\sqrt{1 - x^2}} \, .$$

Do you remember meeting $\dfrac{dx}{\sqrt{1 - x^2}}$? It is got by differentiating $y = \text{arc} \sin x$ (see p. 142) ; hence its integral is $\text{arc} \sin x$, and so

$$\int \sqrt{1 - x^2} \, dx = \frac{x \sqrt{1 - x^2}}{2} + \tfrac{1}{2} \, \text{arc} \sin x + C.$$

You can try now some exercises by yourself ; you will find some at the end of this chapter.

Substitution.   This is the same dodge as explained in Chap. IX, p. 57.   Let us illustrate its application to integration by a few examples.

(1) $\int \sqrt{3+x}\, dx.$

Let $\qquad\qquad\qquad u = 3+x, \quad du = dx\,;$

replace : $\qquad\qquad \int u^{\frac{1}{2}} du = \frac{2}{3} u^{\frac{3}{2}} = \frac{2}{3}(3+x)^{\frac{3}{2}}.$

(2) $\int \dfrac{dx}{\epsilon^x + \epsilon^{-x}}\cdot$

Let $\qquad\quad u = \epsilon^x, \quad \dfrac{du}{dx} = \epsilon^x, \quad \text{and} \quad dx = \dfrac{du}{\epsilon^x}\,;$

so that $\displaystyle\int \frac{dx}{\epsilon^x + \epsilon^{-x}} = \int \frac{du}{\epsilon^x(\epsilon^x + \epsilon^{-x})} = \int \frac{du}{u\left(u + \dfrac{1}{u}\right)} = \int \frac{du}{u^2 + 1}\cdot$

$\dfrac{du}{1+u^2}$ is the result of differentiating arc tan u.

Hence the integral is arc tan ϵ^x.

(3) $\displaystyle\int \frac{dx}{x^2 + 2x + 3} = \int \frac{dx}{x^2 + 2x + 1 + 2} = \int \frac{dx}{(x+1)^2 + (\sqrt{2})^2}\cdot$

Let $\qquad\qquad\qquad u = x+1, \quad du = dx\,;$

then the integral becomes $\displaystyle\int \frac{du}{u^2 + (\sqrt{2})^2}\,;$ but $\dfrac{du}{u^2 + a^2}$ is the result of differentiating $\dfrac{1}{a}$ arc tan $\dfrac{u}{a}\cdot$

Hence one has finally $\dfrac{1}{\sqrt{2}}$ arc tan $\dfrac{x+1}{\sqrt{2}}$ for the value of the given integral.

Formulæ of Reduction are special forms applicable chiefly to binomial and trigonometrical expressions that have to be integrated, and have to be reduced into some form of which the integral is known.

Rationalization, and *Factorization of Denominator* are dodges applicable in special cases, but they do not admit of any short or general explanation. Much practice is needed to become familiar with these preparatory processes.

The following example shows how the process of splitting into partial fractions, which we learned in Chap. XIII, p. 101, can be made use of in integration.

Take again $\int \dfrac{dx}{x^2 + 2x - 3}$; if we split $\dfrac{1}{x^2 + 2x - 3}$ into partial fractions, this becomes (see pp. 193–4) :

$$\frac{1}{4}\left[\int\frac{dx}{x-1} - \int\frac{dx}{x+3}\right] = \frac{1}{4}\left[\log_\epsilon(x-1) - \log_\epsilon(x+3)\right]$$
$$= \frac{1}{4}\log_\epsilon \frac{x-1}{x+3}.$$

Notice that the same integral can be expressed sometimes in more than one way (which are equivalent to one another).

Pitfalls. A beginner is liable to overlook certain points that a practised hand would avoid ; such as the use of factors that are equivalent to either zero or infinity, and the occurrence of indeterminate quantities such as $\frac{0}{0}$. There is no golden rule that will meet every possible case. Nothing but practice and intelligent care will avail. An example of a pitfall which had to be circumvented arose in Chap. XVIII, pp. 165–6, when we came to the problem of integrating $x^{-1}\,dx$.

Triumphs. By triumphs must be understood the successes with which the calculus has been applied to the solution of problems otherwise intractable. Often in the consideration of physical relations one is able to build up an expression for the law governing the interaction of the parts or of the forces that govern them, such expression being naturally in the form of a *differential equation,* that is an equation containing differential coefficients with or without other algebraic quantities.

And when such a differential equation has been found, one can get no further until it has been integrated. Generally it is much easier to state the appropriate differential equation than to solve it : the real trouble begins then only when one wants to integrate, unless indeed the equation is seen to possess some standard form of which the integral is known, and then the triumph is easy. The equation which results from integrating a differential equation is called * its " solution " ; and it is quite astonishing how in many cases the solution looks as if it had no relation to the differential equation of which it is the integrated form. The solution often seems as different from the original expression as a butterfly does from the caterpillar that it was. Who would have supposed that such an innocent thing as

$$\frac{dy}{dx} = \frac{1}{a^2 - x^2}$$

could blossom out into

$$y = \frac{1}{2a} \log_\epsilon \frac{a+x}{a-x} + C?$$

yet the latter is the *solution* of the former.

As a last example, let us work out the above together.

By partial fractions,

$$\frac{1}{a^2 - x^2} = \frac{1}{2a(a+x)} + \frac{1}{2a(a-x)},$$

$$dy = \frac{dx}{2a(a+x)} + \frac{dx}{2a(a-x)},$$

* This means that the actual result of solving it is called its " solution ". But many mathematicians would say, with Professor Forsyth, " every differential equation *is considered as solved* when the value of the dependent variable is expressed as a function of the independent variable by means either of known functions, or of integrals, whether the integrations in the latter can or cannot be expressed in terms of functions already known."

$$y = \frac{1}{2a} \left(\int \frac{dx}{a+x} + \int \frac{dx}{a-x} \right)$$

$$= \frac{1}{2a} \left(\log_\epsilon (a+x) - \log_\epsilon (a-x) \right)$$

$$= \frac{1}{2a} \log_\epsilon \frac{a+x}{a-x} + C.$$

Not a very difficult metamorphosis !

There are whole treatises, such as Boole's *Differential Equations*, devoted to the subject of thus finding the " solutions " for different original forms.

EXERCISES XIX

(See page 248 for Answers)

(1) Find $\int \sqrt{a^2 - x^2}\, dx$.   (2) Find $\int x \log_\epsilon x\, dx$.

(3) Find $\int x^a \log_\epsilon x\, dx$.   (4) Find $\int \epsilon^x \cos \epsilon^x\, dx$.

(5) Find $\int \frac{1}{x} \cos (\log_\epsilon x)\, dx$.   (6) Find $\int x^2 \epsilon^x\, dx$.

(7) Find $\int \frac{(\log_\epsilon x)^a}{x}\, dx$.   (8) Find $\int \frac{dx}{x \log_\epsilon x}$.

(9) Find $\int \frac{5x+1}{x^2 + x - 2}\, dx$.   (10) Find $\int \frac{(x^2 - 3)\, dx}{x^3 - 7x + 6}$.

(11) Find $\int \frac{b\, dx}{x^2 - a^2}$.   (12) Find $\int \frac{4x\, dx}{x^4 - 1}$.

(13) Find $\int \frac{dx}{1 - x^4}$.   (14) Find $\int \frac{x\, dx}{\sqrt{a^2 - b^2 x^2}}$.

(15) Use the substitution $\frac{1}{x} = \frac{b}{a} \cosh u$ to show that

$$\int \frac{dx}{x\sqrt{a^2 - b^2 x^2}} = \frac{1}{a} \log_\epsilon \frac{a - \sqrt{a^2 - b^2 x^2}}{x} + C.$$

CHAPTER XXI

FINDING SOLUTIONS

In this chapter we go to work finding solutions to some important differential equations, using for this purpose the processes shown in the preceding chapters.

The beginner, who now knows how easy most of those processes are in themselves, will here begin to realize that integration is *an art*. As in all arts, so in this, facility can be acquired only by diligent and regular practice. He who would attain that facility must work out examples, and more examples, and yet more examples, such as are found abundantly in all the regular treatises on the Calculus. Our purpose here must be to afford the briefest introduction to serious work.

Example 1. Find the solution of the differential equation

$$ay + b\frac{dy}{dx} = 0.$$

Transposing, we have

$$b\frac{dy}{dx} = -ay.$$

Now the mere inspection of this relation tells us that we have got to do with a case in which $\frac{dy}{dx}$ is proportional to y. If we think of the curve which will represent y as a function of x, it will be such that its slope at any point will be proportional to the ordinate at that point, and will be a negative slope if y is positive. So obviously the curve will be a die-away curve (p. 129), and the solution will contain ϵ^{-x} as a factor. But, without presuming on this bit of sagacity, let us go to work.

As both y and dy occur in the equation and on opposite sides, we can do nothing until we get both y and dy to one side, and dx to the other. To do this, we must split our usually inseparable companions dy and dx from one another.

$$\frac{dy}{y} = -\frac{a}{b}\,dx.$$

Having done the deed, we now can see that both sides have got into a shape that is integrable, because we recognize $\frac{dy}{y}$, or $\frac{1}{y}\,dy$, as a differential that we have met with (pp. 122–3) when differentiating logarithms. So we may at once write down the instructions to integrate,

$$\int\frac{dy}{y} = \int -\frac{a}{b}\,dx\;;$$

and doing the two integrations, we have :

$$\log_\epsilon y = -\frac{a}{b}\,x + \log_\epsilon C,$$

where $\log_\epsilon C$ is the yet undetermined constant * of integration. Then, delogarizing, we get :

$$y = C\epsilon^{-\frac{a}{b}x},$$

which is *the solution* required. Now, this solution looks quite unlike the original differential equation from which it was constructed : yet to an expert mathematician they both convey the same information as to the way in which y depends on x.

---

* We may write down any form of constant as the " constant of integration ", and the form $\log_\epsilon C$ is adopted here by preference, because the other terms in this line of equation are, or are treated as logarithms ; and it saves complications afterward if the added constant be *of the same kind*.

Now, as to the C, its meaning depends on the initial value of y. For if we put $x = 0$ in order to see what value y then has, we find that this makes $y = C\epsilon^{-0}$; and as $\epsilon^{-0} = 1$, we see that C is nothing else than the particular value * of y at starting. This we may call y_0, and so write the solution as

$$y = y_0 \epsilon^{-\frac{a}{b}x}.$$

Example 2.

Let us take as an example to solve

$$ay + b\frac{dy}{dx} = g,$$

where g is a constant. Again, inspecting the equation will suggest, (1) that somehow or other ϵ^x will come into the solution, and (2) that if at any part of the curve y becomes either a maximum or a minimum, so that $\frac{dy}{dx} = 0$, then y will have the value $= \frac{g}{a}$. But let us go to work as before, separating the differentials and trying to transform the thing into some integrable shape.

$$b\frac{dy}{dx} = g - ay \, ;$$

$$\frac{dy}{dx} = \frac{a}{b}\left(\frac{g}{a} - y\right) ;$$

$$\frac{dy}{y - \dfrac{g}{a}} = -\frac{a}{b}\,dx.$$

Now we have done our best to get nothing but y and dy on one side, and nothing but dx on the other. But is the result on the left side integrable?

---

* Compare what was said about the " constant of integration ", with reference to Fig. 48 on p. 156, and Fig. 51 on p. 158.

It is of the same form as the result on pp. 122–3 ; so, writing the instructions to integrate, we have :

$$\int \frac{dy}{y - \dfrac{g}{a}} = - \int \frac{a}{b}\, dx \; ;$$

and, doing the integration, and adding the appropriate constant,

$$\log_\epsilon\left(y - \frac{g}{a}\right) = - \frac{a}{b}\, x + \log_\epsilon C \; ;$$

whence

$$y - \frac{g}{a} = C\epsilon^{-\frac{a}{b}x} \; ;$$

and finally,

$$y = \frac{g}{a} + C\epsilon^{-\frac{a}{b}x} \, ,$$

which is *the solution.*

If the condition is laid down that $y = 0$ when $x = 0$ we can find C ; for then the exponential becomes $= 1$; and we have

$$0 = \frac{g}{a} + C,$$

or

$$C = - \frac{g}{a}.$$

Putting in this value, the solution becomes

$$y = \frac{g}{a}\left(1 - \epsilon^{-\frac{a}{b}x}\right).$$

But further, if x grows indefinitely, y will grow to a maximum ; for when $x = \infty$, the exponential $= 0$, giving $y_{\text{max.}} = \dfrac{g}{a}$. Substituting this, we get finally

$$y = y_{\text{max.}}\left(1 - \epsilon^{-\frac{a}{b}x}\right).$$

This result is also of importance in physical science.

———————

Before proceeding to the next example, it is necessary to discuss two integrals which are of great importance in physics and engineering. These seem to be very elusive as, when either of them is tackled, it turns partly into the other. Yet this very fact helps us to determine their values. Let us denote these integrals by S and C, where

$$S = \int \epsilon^{pt} \sin kt \,.\, dt, \quad \text{and} \quad C = \int \epsilon^{pt} \cos kt \,.\, dt,$$

where p and k are constants.

To tackle these formidable-looking integrals, we resort to the device of integrating by parts, the general formula of which is (see page 188)

$$\int u \, dv = uv - \int v \, du.$$

For this purpose, write $u = \epsilon^{pt}$ and $dv = \sin kt \,.\, dt$ in S; then $du = p\epsilon^{pt} \, dt$, and $v = \int \sin kt \,.\, dt = -\frac{1}{k} \cos kt$, omitting temporarily the constant.

Inserting these values, the integral S becomes

$$S = \int \epsilon^{pt} \sin kt \,.\, dt = -\frac{1}{k} \epsilon^{pt} \cos kt - \int -\frac{1}{k} \cos kt \,.\, p\epsilon^{pt} \, dt$$

$$= -\frac{1}{k} \epsilon^{pt} \cos kt + \frac{p}{k} \int \epsilon^{pt} \cos kt \,.\, dt$$

$$= -\frac{1}{k} \epsilon^{pt} \cos kt + \frac{p}{k} C. \quad \dots\dots\dots\dots\dots(i)$$

Thus the dodge of integrating by parts turns S partly into C. But let us look at C. Writing $u = \epsilon^{pt}$, as before, $dv = \cos kt \,.\, dt$, then $v = \frac{1}{k} \sin kt$; hence, the rule for integrating by parts gives

$$C = \int \epsilon^{pt} \cos kt \,.\, dt = \frac{1}{k} \epsilon^{pt} \sin kt - \frac{p}{k} \int \epsilon^{pt} \sin kt \,.\, dt$$

$$= \frac{1}{k} \epsilon^{pt} \sin kt - \frac{p}{k} S. \quad \dots\dots\dots\dots\dots(ii)$$

The facts that S turns partly into C, and C partly into S might lead you to think that the integrals are intractable, but from the relations (i) and (ii), which may be regarded as two equations in S and C, the integrals themselves may be readily deduced.

Thus, substitute in (i) the value of C from (ii), then

$$S = -\frac{1}{k}\epsilon^{pt}\cos kt + \frac{p}{k}\left(\frac{1}{k}\epsilon^{pt}\sin kt - \frac{p}{k}S\right)$$

or

$$S\left(\frac{p^2}{k^2}+1\right) = \frac{1}{k^2}\epsilon^{pt}(p\sin kt - k\cos kt),$$

from which

$$S = \frac{\epsilon^{pt}}{p^2+k^2}(p\sin kt - k\cos kt).$$

The integral C may be obtained in like manner by inserting in (ii) the equivalent of S given by (i) ; the final result is

$$C = \frac{\epsilon^{pt}}{p^2+k^2}(p\cos kt + k\sin kt).$$

We have, therefore, the following very important integrals to add to our list, namely :

$$\int \epsilon^{pt}\sin kt \,.\, dt = \frac{\epsilon^{pt}}{p^2+k^2}(p\cdot\sin kt - k\cos kt) + E,$$

$$\int \epsilon^{pt}\cos kt \,.\, dt = \frac{\epsilon^{pt}}{p^2+k^2}(p\cos kt + k\sin kt) + F,$$

where E and F are the constants of integration.

Example 3.

Let

$$ay + b\frac{dy}{dt} = g \,.\, \sin 2\pi nt.$$

First divide through by b.

$$\frac{dy}{dt} + \frac{a}{b}y = \frac{g}{b}\sin 2\pi nt.$$

Now, as it stands, the left side is not integrable. But it can be made so by the artifice—and this is where skill and practice suggest a plan—of multiplying all the terms by $\epsilon^{\frac{a}{b}t}$, giving us :

$$\frac{dy}{dt}\epsilon^{\frac{a}{b}t} + \frac{a}{b}y\epsilon^{\frac{a}{b}t} = \frac{g}{b}\epsilon^{\frac{a}{b}t} \cdot \sin 2\pi nt,$$

For if $u = y\epsilon^{\frac{a}{b}t}$, $\frac{du}{dt} = \frac{dy}{dt}\epsilon^{\frac{a}{b}t} + \frac{a}{b}y\epsilon^{\frac{a}{b}t}$.

The equation thus becomes

$$\frac{du}{dt} = \frac{g}{b}\epsilon^{\frac{a}{b}t}\sin 2\pi nt.$$

Hence, on integrating, gives

$$u \text{ or } y\epsilon^{\frac{a}{b}t} = \frac{g}{b}\int \epsilon^{\frac{a}{b}t}\sin 2\pi nt \cdot dt + K.$$

But the right-hand integral is of the same form as S which has just been evaluated ; hence putting $p = \frac{a}{b}$ and $k = 2\pi n$;

$$y\epsilon^{\frac{a}{b}t} = \frac{g\epsilon^{\frac{a}{b}t}}{a^2 + 4\pi^2 n^2 b^2}(a\sin 2\pi nt - 2\pi nb\cos 2\pi nt) + K,$$

or $\qquad y = g\left\{\frac{a\cdot\sin 2\pi nt - 2\pi nb\cdot\cos 2\pi nt}{a^2 + 4\pi^2 n^2 b^2}\right\} + K\epsilon^{-\frac{a}{b}t}.$

To simplify still further, let us imagine an angle ϕ such that $\tan\phi = 2\pi nb/a$.

Then $\sin\phi = \dfrac{2\pi nb}{\sqrt{a^2 + 4\pi^2 n^2 b^2}}$, and $\cos\phi = \dfrac{a}{\sqrt{a^2 + 4\pi^2 n^2 b^2}}$.

Substituting these, we get :

$$y = g\frac{\cos\phi\cdot\sin 2\pi nt - \sin\phi\cdot\cos 2\pi nt}{\sqrt{a^2 + 4\pi^2 n^2 b^2}},$$

or $\qquad y = g\dfrac{\sin(2\pi nt - \phi)}{\sqrt{a^2 + 4\pi^2 n^2 b^2}},$

which is *the solution* desired, omitting the constant which dies out.

This is indeed none other than the equation of an alternating electric current, where g represents the amplitude of the electromotive force, n the frequency, a the resistance, b the coefficient of self-induction of the circuit, and ϕ is an angle of lag.

Example 4.

Suppose that $\qquad M\,dx + N\,dy = 0.$

We could integrate this expression directly, if M were a function of x only, and N a function of y only ; but, if both M and N are functions that depend on both x and y, how are we to integrate it? Is it itself an exact differential? That is : have M and N each been formed by partial differentiation from some common function U, or not? If they have, then

$$\frac{\partial U}{\partial x} = M, \quad \text{and} \quad \frac{\partial U}{\partial y} = N.$$

And if such a common function exists, then

$$\frac{\partial U}{\partial x}\,dx + \frac{\partial U}{\partial y}\,dy,$$

is an exact differential (compare pp. 146–7).

Now the test of the matter is this. If the expression is an exact differential, it must be true that

$$\frac{dM}{dy} = \frac{dN}{dx} ;$$

for then $\qquad \dfrac{d(dU)}{dx\,dy} = \dfrac{d(dU)}{dy\,dx},$

which is necessarily true.

Take as an illustration the equation

$$(1 + 3xy)\,dx + x^2\,dy = 0.$$

Is this an exact differential or not? Apply the test.

$$\frac{d(1 + 3xy)}{dy} = 3x ; \qquad \frac{d(x^2)}{dx} = 2x,$$

which do not agree. Therefore, it is not an exact differential, and the two functions $1 + 3xy$ and x^2 have not come from a common original function.

It is possible in such cases to discover, however, *an integrating factor*, that is to say, a factor such that if both are multiplied by this factor, the expression will become an exact differential. There is no one rule for discovering such an integrating factor ; but experience will usually suggest one. In the present instance $2x$ will act as such. Multiplying by $2x$, we get

$$(2x + 6x^2y)\,dx + 2x^3dy = 0.$$

Now apply the test to this.

$$\frac{d(2x + 6x^2y)}{dy} = 6x^2 ; \qquad \frac{d(2x^3)}{dx} = 6x^2,$$

which agrees. Hence this is an exact differential, and may be integrated. Now, if $w = 2x^3y$,

$$dw = 6x^2y\,dx + 2x^3dy.$$

Hence $$\int 6x^2y\,dx + \int 2x^3\,dy = w = 2x^3y ;$$

so that we get $$U = x^2 + 2x^3y + C.$$

Example 5.   Let $\dfrac{d^2y}{dt^2} + n^2y = 0.$

In this case we have a differential equation of the second degree, in which y appears in the form of a second differential coefficient, as well as in person. Transposing, we have

$$\frac{d^2y}{dt^2} = -n^2y.$$

It appears from this that we have to do with a function such that its second differential coefficient is proportional to itself, but with reversed sign. In Chapter XV we found that there was such a function—namely, the *sine* (or the *cosine* also) which possessed this property. So, without further ado, we may infer that the solution will be of the form

$$y = A \sin (pt + q).$$

However, let us go to work.

Multiply both sides of the original equation by $2\dfrac{dy}{dt}$ and integrate, giving us $2\dfrac{d^2y}{dt^2}\dfrac{dy}{dt}+2n^2y\dfrac{dy}{dt}=0$, and, as

$$2\frac{d^2y}{dt^2}\frac{dy}{dt}=\frac{d\left(\dfrac{dy}{dt}\right)^2}{dt}, \quad \left(\frac{dy}{dt}\right)^2+n^2(y^2-C^2)=\mathbf{0},$$

C being a constant. Then, taking the square roots,

$$\frac{dy}{dt}=n\sqrt{C^2-y^2} \quad \text{and} \quad \frac{dy}{\sqrt{C^2-y^2}}=n\cdot dt.$$

But it can be shown that (see p. 142)

$$\frac{1}{\sqrt{C^2-y^2}}=\frac{d\left(\text{arc sin }\dfrac{y}{C}\right)}{dy};$$

whence, passing from angles to sines,

$$\text{arc sin }\frac{y}{C}=nt+C_1 \quad \text{and} \quad y=C\sin{(nt+C_1)},$$

where C_1 is a constant angle that comes in by integration.

Or, preferably, this may be written

$$y=A\sin nt+B\cos nt, \quad \text{which is the solution.}$$

Example 6. $\qquad\qquad \dfrac{d^2y}{dx^2}-n^2y=0.$

Here we have obviously to deal with a function y which is such that its second differential coefficient is proportional to itself. The only function we know that has this property is the exponential function (see p. 118), and we may be certain therefore that the solution of the equation will be of that form.

Proceeding as before, by multiplying through by $2\dfrac{dy}{dx}$, and integrating, we get $2\dfrac{d^2y}{dx^2}\dfrac{dy}{dx} - 2n^2y\,\dfrac{dy}{dx} = 0$, and, as

$$2\frac{d^2y}{dx^2}\frac{dy}{dx} = \frac{d\left(\dfrac{dy}{dx}\right)^2}{dx}, \quad \left(\frac{dy}{dx}\right)^2 - n^2(y^2 + c^2) = 0,$$

$$\frac{dy}{dx} - n\sqrt{y^2 + c^2} = 0,$$

where c is a constant, and $\dfrac{dy}{\sqrt{y^2 + c^2}} = n\,dx.$

To integrate this equation it is simpler to use hyperbolic functions. (See p. 144.)

Let $\quad y = c \sinh u$, then $dy = c \cosh u\,du$, and

$$y^2 + c^2 = c^2(\sinh^2 u + 1) = c^2 \cosh^2 u.$$

$$\therefore \int \frac{dy}{\sqrt{y^2 + c^2}} = \int \frac{c \cosh u\,du}{c \cosh u} = \int du = u.$$

Hence, the integral of the equation

$$n\int dx = \int \frac{dy}{\sqrt{y^2 + c^2}}$$

is $\qquad\qquad nx + K = u,$

where K is the constant of integration, and $c \sinh u = y.$

$$\therefore \sinh(nx + K) = \sinh u = \frac{y}{c},$$

or
$$\begin{aligned}
y &= c \sinh(nx + K)\\
&= \tfrac{1}{2}c\,(\epsilon^{nx+K} - \epsilon^{-nx-K})\\
&= A\epsilon^{nx} + B\epsilon^{-nx},
\end{aligned}$$

where $A = \tfrac{1}{2}c\epsilon^K$ and $B = -\tfrac{1}{2}c\epsilon^{-K}.$

This solution, which at first sight does not look as if it had anything to do with the original equation, shows that y consists of two terms, one of which grows logarithmically as x increases, while the other term dies away as x increases.

Example 7.

Let
$$b\,\frac{d^2y}{dt^2} + a\,\frac{dy}{dt} + gy = 0.$$

Examination of this expression will show that, if $b = 0$, it has the form of Example 1, the solution of which was a negative exponential. On the other hand, if $a = 0$, its form becomes the same as that of Example 6, the solution of which is the sum of a positive and a negative exponential. It is therefore not very surprising to find that the solution of the present example is

$$y = (\epsilon^{-mt})(A\epsilon^{nt} + B\epsilon^{-nt}),$$

where
$$m = \frac{a}{2b} \quad \text{and} \quad n = \frac{\sqrt{a^2 - 4bg}}{2b}.$$

The steps by which this solution is reached are not given here; they may be found in advanced treatises.

Example 8.

$$\frac{d^2y}{dt^2} = a^2\,\frac{d^2y}{dx^2}.$$

It was seen (pp. 148–9) that this equation was derived from the original

$$y = F(x + at) + f(x - at),$$

where F and f were any arbitrary functions of t.

Another way of dealing with it is to transform it by a change of variables into

$$\frac{d^2y}{du \cdot dv} = 0,$$

where $u = x + at$, and $v = x - at$, leading to the same general solution. If we consider a case in which F vanishes, then we have simply

$$y = f(x - at);$$

and this merely states that, at the time $t = 0$, y is a particular function of x, and may be looked upon as denoting that the curve of the relation of y to x has a particular shape. Then any change in the value of t is equivalent simply to an alteration in the origin from which x is reckoned. That is to say, it indicates that, the form of the function being conserved, it is propagated along the x direction with a uniform velocity a ; so that whatever the value of the ordinate y at any particular time t_0 at any particular point x_0, the same value of y will appear at the subsequent time t_1 at a point further along, the abscissa of which is $x_0 + a(t_1 - t_0)$. In this case the simplified equation represents the propagation of a wave (of any form) at a uniform speed along the x direction.

If the differential equation had been written

$$m \frac{d^2y}{dt^2} = k \frac{d^2y}{dx^2} ,$$

the solution would have been the same, but the velocity of propagation would have had the value

$$a = \sqrt{\frac{k}{m}} .$$

EXERCISES XX

(See page 248 for Answers)

Try to solve the following equations.

(1) $\dfrac{dT}{d\theta} = \mu T$, given that μ is constant, and when $\theta = 0$, $T = T_0$.

(2) $\dfrac{d^2s}{dt^2} = a$, where a is constant.   When $t = 0$, $s = 0$ and $\dfrac{ds}{dt} = u$.

(3) $\dfrac{di}{dt} + 2i = \sin 3t$, it being known that $i = 0$ when $t = 0$.

(*Hint.*   Multiply out by ϵ^{2t} and refer to pp. 200–1.)

CHAPTER XXII

A LITTLE MORE ABOUT CURVATURE OF CURVES

In Chapter XII we have learned how we can find out which way a curve is curved, that is, whether it curves upwards or downwards towards the right. This gave us no indication whatever as to *how much* the curve is curved, or, in other words, what is its *curvature*.

By *curvature* of a line, we mean the amount of bending or deflection taking place along a certain length of the line, say along a portion of the line the length of which is one unit of length (the same unit which is used to measure the radius, whether it be one inch, one foot, or any other unit). For instance, consider two circular paths of centre O and O' and of equal lengths AB, $A'B'$ (see Fig. 64). When passing from

Fig. 64.

A to B along the arc AB of the first one, one changes one's direction from AP to BQ, since at A one faces in the direction

AP and at *B* one faces in the direction *BQ*. In other words, in walking from *A* to *B* one unconsciously turns round through the angle *PCQ*, which is equal to the angle *AOB*. Similarly, in passing from *A'* to *B'*, along the arc *A'B'*, of equal length to *AB*, on the second path, one turns round through the angle *P'C'Q'*, which is equal to the angle *A'O'B'*, obviously *greater* than the corresponding angle *AOB*. The second path bends therefore more than the first for an equal length.

This fact is expressed by saying that the *curvature* of the second path is greater than that of the first one. The larger the circle, the lesser the bending, that is, the lesser the curvature. If the radius of the first circle is 2, 3, 4, ... etc. times greater than the radius of the second, then the angle of bending or deflection along an arc of unit length will be 2, 3, 4, ... etc. times less on the first circle than on the second, that is, it will be $\frac{1}{2}$, $\frac{1}{3}$, $\frac{1}{4}$, ... etc. of the bending or deflection along the arc of same length on the second circle. In other words, the *curvature* of the first circle will be $\frac{1}{2}$, $\frac{1}{3}$, $\frac{1}{4}$, ... etc. of that of the second circle. We see that, as the radius becomes 2, 3, 4, ... etc. times greater, the curvature becomes 2, 3, 4, ... etc. times smaller, and this is expressed by saying that *the curvature of a circle is inversely proportional to the radius of the circle*, or

$$\text{curvature} = k \times \frac{1}{\text{radius}} \, ,$$

where *k* is a constant. It is agreed to take *k* = 1, so that

$$\text{curvature} = \frac{1}{\text{radius}} \, ,$$

always.

If the radius becomes indefinitely great, the curvature becomes $\frac{1}{\text{infinity}}$ = zero, since when the denominator of a fraction is indefinitely large, the value of the fraction is indefinitely small. For this reason mathematicians sometimes consider a straight line as an arc of circle of infinite radius, or zero curvature.

In the case of a circle, which is perfectly symmetrical and uniform, so that the curvature is the same at every point of its circumference, the above method of expressing the curvature is perfectly definite. In the case of any other curve, however, the curvature is not the same at different points, and it may differ considerably even for two points fairly close to one another. It would not then be accurate to take the amount of bending or deflection between two points as a measure of the curvature of the arc between these points, unless this arc is very small, in fact, unless it is indefinitely small.

If then we consider a very small arc such as AB (see Fig. 65), and if we draw such a circle that an arc AB of this circle

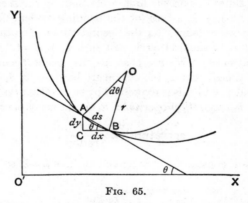

Fig. 65.

coincides with the arc AB of the curve more closely than would be the case with any other circle, then the curvature of this circle may be taken as the curvature of the arc AB of the curve. The smaller the arc AB, the easier it will be to find a circle an arc of which most nearly coincides with the arc AB of the curve. When A and B are very near one another, so that AB is so small so that the length ds of the arc AB is practically negligible, then the coincidence of the two arcs, of circle and of curve, may be considered as being practically perfect, and the curvature of the curve at the point A (or B), being then the same as the curvature of the circle, will be expressed by the reciprocal of the radius of this circle, that is, by $\dfrac{1}{OA}$, according to our way of measuring curvature, explained above.

Now, at first, you may think that, if AB is very small, then the circle must be very small also. A little thinking will, however, cause you to perceive that it is by no means necessarily so, and that the circle may have any size, according to the amount of bending of the curve along this very small arc AB. In fact, if the curve is almost flat at that point, the circle will be extremely large. This circle is called the *circle of curvature*, or the *osculating circle* at the point considered. Its radius is the *radius of curvature* of the curve at that particular point.

If the arc AB is represented by ds and the angle AOB by $d\theta$, then, if r is the radius of curvature,

$$ds = r\,d\theta \quad \text{or} \quad \frac{d\theta}{ds} = \frac{1}{r}.$$

The secant AB makes with the axis OX the angle θ, and it will be seen from the small triangle ABC that $\dfrac{dy}{dx} = \tan\theta$. When AB is indefinitely small, so that B practically coincides with A, the line AB becomes a tangent to the curve at the point A (or B).

Now, $\tan\theta$ depends on the position of the point A (or B, which is supposed to nearly coincide with it), that is, it depends on x, or, in other words, $\tan\theta$ is " a function " of x.

Differentiating with regard to x to get the slope (see p. 93), we get

$$\frac{d\left(\frac{dy}{dx}\right)}{dx} = \frac{d(\tan\theta)}{dx} \quad \text{or} \quad \frac{d^2y}{dx^2} = \sec^2\theta \frac{d\theta}{dx} = \frac{1}{\cos^2\theta}\frac{d\theta}{dx} \text{ (see pp. 139–40) ;}$$

hence

$$\frac{d\theta}{dx} = \cos^2\theta \frac{d^2y}{dx^2}.$$

But $\dfrac{dx}{ds} = \cos\theta$, and for $\dfrac{d\theta}{ds}$ one may write $\dfrac{d\theta}{dx} \times \dfrac{dx}{ds}$; therefore

$$\frac{1}{r} = \frac{d\theta}{ds} = \frac{d\theta}{dx} \times \frac{dx}{ds} = \cos^3\theta \frac{d^2y}{dx^2} = \frac{\frac{d^2y}{dx^2}}{\sec^3\theta} ;$$

but $\sec\theta = \sqrt{1 + \tan^2\theta}$; hence

$$\frac{1}{r} = \frac{\frac{d^2y}{dx^2}}{(\sqrt{1 + \tan^2\theta})^3} = \frac{\frac{d^2y}{dx^2}}{\left\{1 + \left(\frac{dy}{dx}\right)^2\right\}^{\frac{3}{2}}} ;$$

and finally,

$$r = \frac{\left\{1 + \left(\frac{dy}{dx}\right)^2\right\}^{\frac{3}{2}}}{\frac{d^2y}{dx^2}}$$

The numerator, being a square root, may have the sign $+$ or the sign $-$. One must select for it the same sign as the denominator, so as to have r positive always, as a negative radius would have no meaning.

It has been shown (Chapter XII) that if $\dfrac{d^2y}{dx^2}$ is positive, the curve is convex downwards, while if $\dfrac{d^2y}{dx^2}$ is negative, the curve is concave downwards. If $\dfrac{d^2y}{dx^2} = 0$, the radius of curvature is infinitely great, that is, the corresponding portion of the curve is a bit of straight line. This necessarily happens whenever a curve gradually changes from being convex to concave to the axis of x or vice versa. The point where this occurs is called a *point of inflexion*.

The centre of the circle of curvature is called the *centre of curvature*. If its coordinates are x_1, y_1, then the equation of the circle is (see p. 85)

$$(x - x_1)^2 + (y - y_1)^2 = r^2 \; ;$$

hence

$$2(x - x_1)\,dx + 2(y - y_1)\,dy = 0,$$

and

$$x - x_1 + (y - y_1)\frac{dy}{dx} = 0. \quad \text{...............(1)}$$

Why did we differentiate? To get rid of the constant r. This leaves but two unknown constants x_1 and y_1; differentiate again; you shall get rid of one of them. This last differentiation is not quite as easy as it seems; let us do it together; we have :

$$\frac{d(x)}{dx} + \frac{d\left[(y - y_1)\dfrac{dy}{dx}\right]}{dx} = 0 \; ;$$

the numerator of the second term is a product; hence differentiating it gives

$$(y - y_1)\frac{d\left(\dfrac{dy}{dx}\right)}{dx} + \frac{dy}{dx}\frac{d(y - y_1)}{dx} = (y - y_1)\frac{d^2y}{dx^2} + \left(\frac{dy}{dx}\right)^2,$$

so that the result of differentiating (1) is

$$1 + \left(\frac{dy}{dx}\right)^2 + (y - y_1)\frac{d^2y}{dx^2} = 0 \; ;$$

from this we at once get

$$y_1 = y + \frac{1 + \left(\dfrac{dy}{dx}\right)^2}{\dfrac{d^2y}{dx^2}}.$$

Replacing in (1), we get

$$(x - x_1) + \left\{ y - y - \frac{1 + \left(\frac{dy}{dx}\right)^2}{\frac{d^2y}{dx^2}} \right\} \frac{dy}{dx} = 0 ;$$

and finally,
$$x_1 = x - \frac{\frac{dy}{dx}\left\{ 1 + \left(\frac{dy}{dx}\right) \right\}^2}{\frac{d^2y}{dx^2}} ;$$

x_1 and y_1 give the position of the centre of curvature. The use of these formulae will be best seen by carefully going through a few worked-out examples.

Example 1. Find the radius of curvature and the coordinates of the centre of curvature of the curve $y = 2x^2 - x + 3$ at the point $x = 0$.

We have
$$\frac{dy}{dx} = 4x - 1, \quad \frac{d^2y}{dx^2} = 4.$$

$$r = \frac{\pm \left\{ 1 + \left(\frac{dy}{dx}\right)^2 \right\}^{\frac{3}{2}}}{\frac{d^2y}{dx^2}} = \frac{\{1 + (4x-1)^2\}^{\frac{3}{2}}}{4},$$

when $x = 0$; this becomes

$$\frac{\{1 + (-1)^2\}^{\frac{3}{2}}}{4} = \frac{\sqrt{8}}{4} = 0 \cdot 707.$$

If x_1, y_1 are the coordinates of the centre of curvature, then

$$x_1 = x - \frac{\frac{dy}{dx}\left\{ 1 + \left(\frac{dy}{dx}\right)^2 \right\}}{\frac{d^2y}{dx^2}} = x - \frac{(4x-1)\{1 + (4x-1)^2\}}{4}$$

$$= 0 - \frac{(-1)\{1 + (-1)^2\}}{4} = \frac{1}{2}$$

when $x = 0$, $y = 3$, so that

$$y_1 = y + \frac{1 + \left(\frac{dy}{dx}\right)^2}{\frac{d^2y}{dx^2}} = y + \frac{1 + (4x - 1)^2}{4} = 3 + \frac{1 + (-1)^2}{4} = 3\tfrac{1}{2}.$$

Plot the curve and draw the circle; it is both interesting and instructive. The values can be checked easily, as since when $x = 0$, $y = 3$, here

$$x_1{}^2 + (y_1 - 3)^2 = r^2 \quad \text{or} \quad 0\cdot5^2 + 0\cdot5^2 = 0\cdot50 = 0\cdot707^2$$

Example 2. Find the radius of curvature and the position of the centre of curvature of the curve $y^2 = mx$ at the point for which $y = 0$.

Here
$$y = m^{\frac{1}{2}}x^{\frac{1}{2}}, \quad \frac{dy}{dx} = \frac{1}{2}m^{\frac{1}{2}}x^{-\frac{1}{2}} = \frac{m^{\frac{1}{2}}}{2x^{\frac{1}{2}}},$$

$$\frac{d^2y}{dx^2} = -\frac{1}{2} \times \frac{m^{\frac{1}{2}}}{2}x^{-\frac{3}{2}} = -\frac{m^{\frac{1}{2}}}{4x^{\frac{3}{2}}};$$

hence
$$\frac{\pm\left\{1 + \left(\frac{dy}{dx}\right)^2\right\}^{\frac{3}{2}}}{\frac{d^2y}{dx^2}} = \frac{\pm\left\{1 + \frac{m}{4x}\right\}^{\frac{3}{2}}}{-\frac{m^{\frac{1}{2}}}{4x^{\frac{3}{2}}}} = \frac{(4x + m)^{\frac{3}{2}}}{2m^{\frac{1}{2}}},$$

taking the $-$ sign at the numerator, so as to have r positive.

Since, when $y = 0$, $x = 0$, we get $r = \frac{m^{\frac{3}{2}}}{2m^{\frac{1}{2}}} = \frac{m}{2}$.

Also, if x_1, y_1 are the coordinates of the centre,

$$x_1 = x - \frac{\frac{dy}{dx}\left\{1 + \left(\frac{dy}{dx}\right)^2\right\}}{\frac{d^2y}{d^2x}} = x - \frac{\frac{m^{\frac{1}{2}}}{2x^{\frac{1}{2}}}\left\{1 + \frac{m}{4x}\right\}}{-\frac{m^{\frac{1}{2}}}{4x^{\frac{3}{2}}}} = x + \frac{4x + m}{2} = 3x + \frac{m}{2},$$

when $x = 0$, then $x_1 = \frac{m}{2}$.

Also $\quad y_1 = y + \dfrac{1 + \left(\dfrac{dy}{dx}\right)^2}{\dfrac{d^2y}{dx^2}} = m^{\frac{1}{2}} x^{\frac{1}{2}} - \dfrac{1 + \dfrac{m}{4x}}{\dfrac{m^{\frac{1}{2}}}{4x^{\frac{3}{2}}}} = -\dfrac{4x^{\frac{3}{2}}}{m^{\frac{1}{2}}} ;$

when $x = 0$, $y_1 = 0$.

Example 3. Show that the circle is a curve of constant curvature.

If x_1, y_1 are the coordinates of the centre, and R is the radius, the equation of the circle in rectangular coordinates is

$$(x - x_1)^2 + (y - y_1)^2 = R^2 ;$$

Let $x - x_1 = R \cos \theta$, then

$$(y - y_1)^2 = R^2 - R^2 \cos^2\theta = R^2(1 - \cos^2\theta) = R^2 \sin^2\theta,$$
$$\therefore \ y - y_1 = R \sin \theta.$$

R, θ are thus the polar coordinates of any point on the circle referred to its centre as pole.

Since $x - x_1 = R \cos \theta$, and $y - y_1 = R \sin \theta$,

$$\frac{dx}{d\theta} = - R \sin \theta, \quad \frac{dy}{d\theta} = R \cos \theta,$$

$$\therefore \ \frac{dy}{dx} = \frac{dy}{d\theta} \cdot \frac{d\theta}{dx} = - \cot \theta.$$

Further, $\quad \dfrac{d^2y}{dx^2} = - (-\operatorname{cosec}^2\theta)\,\dfrac{d\theta}{dx} = \operatorname{cosec}^2\theta \cdot \left(- \dfrac{\operatorname{cosec}\,\theta}{R}\right)$

$$= - \frac{\operatorname{cosec}^3\theta}{R} \cdot \quad \text{(See Ex. 5, p. 143.)}$$

Hence $\quad r = \dfrac{\pm(1 + \cot^2\theta)^{\frac{3}{2}}}{-\dfrac{\operatorname{cosec}^3\theta}{R}} = \dfrac{R \operatorname{cosec}^3\theta}{\operatorname{cosec}^3\theta} = R.$

Thus the radius of curvature is constant and equal to the radius of the circle.

Example 4. Find the radius of curvature of the curve $x = 2 \cos^3 t$, $y = 2 \sin^3 t$ at any point (x, y).

Here $\qquad dx = -6\cos^2 t \sin t\, dt$ (see Ex. 2, p. 142)

and $\qquad dy = 6\sin^2 t \cos t\, dt.$

$$\therefore \frac{dy}{dx} = -\frac{6\sin^2 t \cos t\, dt}{6\sin t \cos^2 t\, dt} = -\frac{\sin t}{\cos t} = -\tan t\,;$$

Hence $\qquad \dfrac{d^2y}{dx^2} = \dfrac{d}{dt}\,(-\tan t)\,\dfrac{dt}{dx} = \dfrac{-\sec^2 t}{-6\cos^2 t \sin t} = \dfrac{\sec^4 t}{6\sin t}\,.$

$$\therefore r = \frac{\pm(1+\tan^2 t)^{\frac{3}{2}} \times 6\sin t}{\sec^4 t} = \frac{6\sec^3 t \sin t}{\sec^4 t}$$

$$= 6\sin t \cos t = 3\sin 2t, \text{ for } 2\sin t \cos t = \sin 2t.$$

Example 5. Find the radius and the centre of curvature of the curve $y = x^3 - 2x^2 + x - 1$ at points where $x = 0$, $x = 0\cdot 5$ and $x = 1\cdot 0$. Find also the position of the point of inflexion of the curve.

Here $\qquad \dfrac{dy}{dx} = 3x^2 - 4x + 1, \quad \dfrac{d^2y}{dx^2} = 6x - 4.$

$$r = \frac{\{1 + (3x^2 - 4x + 1)^2\}^{\frac{3}{2}}}{6x - 4},$$

$$x_1 = x - \frac{(3x^2 - 4x + 1)\{1 + (3x^2 - 4x + 1)^2\}}{6x - 4},$$

$$y_1 = y + \frac{1 + (3x^2 - 4x + 1)^2}{6x - 4}\,.$$

When $x = 0$, $y = -1$,

$$r = \frac{\sqrt{8}}{4} = 0\cdot 707, \quad x_1 = 0 + \tfrac{1}{2} = 0\cdot 5, \quad y_1 = -1 - \tfrac{1}{2} = -1\cdot 5.$$

Plot the curve, mark the point $x = 0$, $y = -1$, take two points on either side about half an inch away and construct geometrically the circle passing by the three points ; measure the radius and the coordinates of the centre, and compare with the above results. On a diagram, the scale of which was 2 inches = unit length, the construction gave a circle for which $r = 0\cdot 72$, $x_1 = 0\cdot 47$, $y_1 = -1\cdot 53$, a very fair agreement.

When $x = 0.5$, $y = -0.875$,

$$r = \frac{-\{1 + (-0.25)^2\}^{\frac{3}{2}}}{-1} = 1.09,$$

$$x_1 = 0.5 - \frac{-0.25 \times 1.09}{-1} = 0.33,$$

$$y_1 = -0.875 + \frac{1.09}{-1} = -1.96.$$

The diagram gave $r = 0.98$, $x_1 = 0.33$, $y_1 = -1.83$.

When $x = 1$, $y = -1$,

$$r = \frac{(1+0)^{\frac{3}{2}}}{2} = 0.5,$$

$$x_1 = 1 - \frac{0 \times (1+0)}{2} = 1,$$

$$y_1 = -1 + \frac{1 + 0^2}{2} = -0.5.$$

The diagram gave $r = 0.57$, $x_1 = 0.96$, $y_1 = -0.44$.

At the point of inflexion $\frac{d^2y}{dx^2} = 0$, $6x - 4 = 0$, and $x = \frac{2}{3}$; hence $y = 0.925$.

Example 6. Find the radius and centre of curvature of the curve $y = \frac{a}{2}\left\{ \epsilon^{\frac{x}{a}} + \epsilon^{-\frac{x}{a}} \right\}$, at the point for which $x = 0$. (This curve is called the *catenary*, as a hanging chain affects the same slope exactly.) The equation of the curve may be written

$$y = \frac{a}{2}\epsilon^{\frac{x}{a}} + \frac{a}{2}\epsilon^{-\frac{x}{a}};$$

then (see Examples on pp. 124–5),

$$\frac{dy}{dx} = \frac{a}{2} \times \frac{1}{a}\epsilon^{\frac{x}{a}} - \frac{a}{2} \times \frac{1}{a}\epsilon^{-\frac{x}{a}} = \frac{1}{2}\left(\epsilon^{\frac{x}{a}} - \epsilon^{-\frac{x}{a}} \right).$$

Similarly

$$\frac{d^2y}{dx^2} = \frac{1}{2a}\left\{\epsilon^{\frac{x}{a}} + \epsilon^{-\frac{x}{a}}\right\} = \frac{1}{2a} \times \frac{2y}{a} = \frac{y}{a^2},$$

$$r = \frac{\left\{1 + \frac{1}{4}\left(\epsilon^{\frac{x}{a}} - \epsilon^{-\frac{x}{a}}\right)^2\right\}^{\frac{3}{2}}}{\frac{y}{a^2}} = \frac{a^2}{8y}\sqrt{\left(2 + \epsilon^{\frac{2x}{a}} + \epsilon^{-\frac{2x}{a}}\right)^3},$$

since $\epsilon^{\frac{x}{a} - \frac{x}{a}} = \epsilon^0 = 1$, or

$$r = \frac{a^2}{8y}\sqrt{\left(2\epsilon^{\frac{x}{a} - \frac{x}{a}} + \epsilon^{\frac{2x}{a}} + \epsilon^{-\frac{2x}{a}}\right)^3} = \frac{a^2}{8y}\sqrt{\left(\epsilon^{\frac{x}{a}} + \epsilon^{-\frac{x}{a}}\right)^6} = \frac{y^2}{a},$$

when $\qquad x = 0, \quad y = \frac{a}{2}\left(\epsilon^0 + \epsilon^0\right) = a,$

hence $\qquad\qquad r = \frac{a^2}{a} = a.$

The radius of curvature at the vertex is equal to the constant a.

Also when $x = 0$, $x_1 = 0 - \dfrac{0(1+0)}{\dfrac{1}{a}} = 0,$

and $\qquad\qquad y_1 = y + \dfrac{1+0}{\dfrac{1}{a}} = a + a = 2a.$

As defined on p. 144,

$$\frac{1}{2}\left(\epsilon^{\frac{x}{a}} + \epsilon^{-\frac{x}{a}}\right) = \cosh\frac{x}{a},$$

thus the equation of the catenary may be written in the form

$$y = a\cosh\frac{x}{a}.$$

It will therefore be a useful exercise for you to verify the above results from this form of the equation.

You are now sufficiently familiar with this type of problem to work out the following exercises by yourself. You are advised to check your answers by careful plotting of the curve and construction of the circle of curvature, as explained in Example 4.

EXERCISES XXI

(*See page* 249 *for Answers*)

(1) Find the radius of curvature and the position of the centre of curvature of the curve $y = \epsilon^x$ at the point for which $x = 0$.

(2) Find the radius and the centre of curvature of the curve $y = x\left(\dfrac{x}{2} - 1\right)$ at the point for which $x = 2$.

(3) Find the point or points of curvature unity in the curve $y = x^2$.

(4) Find the radius and the centre of curvature of the curve $xy = m$ at the point for which $x = \sqrt{m}$.

(5) Find the radius and the centre of curvature of the curve $y^2 = 4ax$ at the point for which $x = 0$.

(6) Find the radius and the centre of curvature of the curve $y = x^3$ at the points for which $x = \pm 0 \cdot 9$ and also $x = 0$.

(7) Find the radius of curvature and the coordinates of the centre of curvature of the curve

$$y = x^2 - x + 2$$

at the two points for which $x = 0$ and $x = 1$, respectively. Find also the maximum or minimum value of y. Verify graphically all your results.

(8) Find the radius of curvature and the coordinates of the centre of curvature of the curve

$$y = x^3 - x - 1$$

at the points for which $x = -2$, $x = 0$, and $x = 1$.

(9) Find the coordinates of the point or points of inflexion of the curve $y = x^3 + x^2 + 1$.

(10) Find the radius of curvature and the coordinates of the centre of curvature of the curve
$$y = (4x - x^2 - 3)^{\frac{1}{2}}$$
at the points for which $x = 1\cdot2$, $x = 2$ and $x = 2\cdot5$. What is this curve?

(11) Find the radius and the centre of curvature of the curve $y = x^3 - 3x^2 + 2x + 1$ at the points for which $x = 0$, $x = +1\cdot5$. Find also the position of the point of inflexion.

(12) Find the radius and centre of curvature of the curve $y = \sin\theta$ at the points for which $\theta = \dfrac{\pi}{4}$ and $\theta = \dfrac{\pi}{2}$. Find the position of the point of inflexion.

(13) Draw a circle of radius 3, the centre of which has for its coordinates $x = 1$, $y = 0$. Deduce the equation of such a circle from first principles (see p. 85). Find by calculation the radius of curvature and the coordinates of the centre of curvature for several suitable points, as accurately as possible, and verify that you get the known values.

(14) Find the radius and centre of curvature of the curve $y = \cos\theta$ at the points for which $\theta = 0$, $\theta = \dfrac{\pi}{4}$ and $\theta = \dfrac{\pi}{2}$.

(15) Find the radius of curvature and the centre of curvature of the ellipse $\dfrac{x^2}{a^2} + \dfrac{y^2}{b^2} = 1$ at the points for which $x = 0$ and at the points for which $y = 0$.

(16) When a curve is defined by equations in the form
$$x = F(\theta), \quad y = f(\theta),$$
the radius r of curvature is given by
$$r = \left\{ \left(\frac{dx}{d\theta}\right)^2 + \left(\frac{dy}{d\theta}\right)^2 \right\}^{\frac{3}{2}} \bigg/ \left(\frac{dx}{d\theta} \cdot \frac{d^2y}{d\theta^2} - \frac{dy}{d\theta} \cdot \frac{d^2x}{d\theta^2} \right).$$
Can you derive this from the formulae found on p. 212? Apply the formula to find r for the curve
$$x = a(\theta - \sin\theta), \quad y = a(1 - \cos\theta).$$

CHAPTER XXIII

HOW TO FIND THE LENGTH OF AN ARC ON A CURVE

SINCE an arc on any curve is made up of a lot of little bits of straight lines joined end to end, if we could add all these little bits, we would get the length of the arc. But we have seen that to add a lot of little bits together is precisely what is called integration, so that it is likely that, since we know how

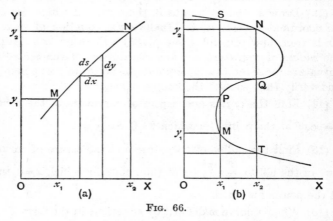

FIG. 66.

to integrate, we can find also the length of an arc on any curve, provided that the equation of the curve is such that it lends itself to integration.

If MN is an arc on any curve, the length s of which is required (see Fig. 66a), if we call " a little bit " of the arc ds, then we see at once that

$$(ds)^2 = (dx)^2 + (dy)^2,$$

or either

$$ds = \sqrt{1 + \left(\frac{dx}{dy}\right)^2}\, dy \quad \text{or} \quad ds = \sqrt{1 + \left(\frac{dy}{dx}\right)^2}\, dx.$$

Now the arc MN is made up of the sum of all the little bits ds between M and N, that is, between x_1 and x_2, or between y_1 and y_2, so that we get either

$$s = \int_{x_1}^{x_2} \sqrt{1 + \left(\frac{dy}{dx}\right)^2}\, dx \quad \text{or} \quad s = \int_{y_1}^{y_2} \sqrt{1 + \left(\frac{dx}{dy}\right)^2}\, dy.$$

That is all !

The second integral is useful when there are several points of the curve corresponding to the given values of x (as in Fig. 66b). In this case the integral between x_1 and x_2 leaves a doubt as to the exact portion of the curve, the length of which is required. It may be ST, instead of MN, or SQ ; by integrating between y_1 and y_2 the uncertainty is removed, and in this case one should use the second integral.

If instead of x and y coordinates—or Cartesian coordinates, as they are named from the French mathematician Descartes, who invented them—we have r and θ coordinates (or polar coordinates, see p. 182) ; then, if MN be a small arc of length

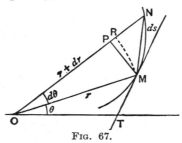

Fig. 67.

ds on any curve, the length s of which is required (see Fig. 67), O being the pole, then the distance ON will generally differ from OM by a small amount dr. If the small angle

MON is called $d\theta$, then, the polar coordinates of the point M being θ and r, those of N are $(\theta + d\theta)$ and $(r + dr)$. Let MP be perpendicular to ON, and let $OR = OM$; then $RN = dr$, and this is very nearly the same as PN, as long as $d\theta$ is a very small angle. Also $RM = r\,d\theta$, and RM is very nearly equal to PM, and the arc MN is very nearly equal to the chord MN. In fact we can write $PN = dr$, $PM = r\,d\theta$, and arc $MN =$ chord MN without appreciable error, so that we have:

$$(ds)^2 = (\text{chord } MN)^2 = \overline{PN}^2 + \overline{PM}^2 = dr^2 + r^2 d\theta^2.$$

Dividing by $d\theta^2$ we get $\left(\dfrac{ds}{d\theta}\right)^2 = r^2 + \left(\dfrac{dr}{d\theta}\right)^2$; hence

$$\frac{ds}{d\theta} = \sqrt{r^2 + \left(\frac{dr}{d\theta}\right)^2} \quad \text{and} \quad ds = \sqrt{r^2 + \left(\frac{dr}{d\theta}\right)^2}\,d\theta;$$

hence, since the length s is made up of the sum of all the little bits ds, between values of $\theta = \theta_1$ and $\theta = \theta_2$, we have

$$s = \int_{\theta_1}^{\theta_2} ds = \int_{\theta_1}^{\theta_2} \sqrt{r^2 + \left(\frac{dr}{d\theta}\right)^2}\,d\theta.$$

We can proceed at once to work out a few examples.

Example 1. The equation of a circle, the centre of which is at the origin—or intersection of the axis of x with the axis of y—is $x^2 + y^2 = r^2$; find the length of an arc of one quadrant.

$$y^2 = r^2 - x^2 \text{ and } 2y\,dy = -2x\,dx, \text{ so that } \frac{dy}{dx} = -\frac{x}{y};$$

hence

$$s = \int \sqrt{\left[1 + \left(\frac{dy}{dx}\right)^2\right]}\,dx = \int \sqrt{\left(1 + \frac{x^2}{y^2}\right)}\,dx;$$

and since $y^2 = r^2 - x^2$,

$$s = \int \sqrt{\left(1 + \frac{x^2}{r^2 - x^2}\right)}\,dx = \int \frac{r\,dx}{\sqrt{(r^2 - x^2)}}.$$

The length we want—one quadrant—extends from a point for which $x = 0$ to another point for which $x = r$. We express this by writing

$$s = \int_{x=0}^{x=r} \frac{r\, dx}{\sqrt{(r^2 - x^2)}},$$

or, more simply, by writing

$$s = \int_0^r \frac{r\, dx}{\sqrt{(r^2 - x^2)}},$$

the 0 and r to the right of the sign of integration merely meaning that the integration is only to be performed on a portion of the curve, namely, that between $x = 0$, $x = r$, as we have seen (p. 175).

Here is a fresh integral for you! Can you manage it?

On p. 142 we have differentiated $y = \text{arc}\,(\sin x)$ and found $\frac{dy}{dx} = \frac{1}{\sqrt{(1 - x^2)}}$. If you have tried all sorts of variations of the given examples (as you ought to have done!), you perhaps tried to differentiate something like $y = a\,\text{arc}\left(\sin\frac{x}{a}\right)$, which gave

$$\frac{dy}{dx} = \frac{a}{\sqrt{(a^2 - x^2)}} \quad \text{or} \quad dy = \frac{a\, dx}{\sqrt{(a^2 - x^2)}},$$

that is, just the same expression as the one we have to integrate here.

Hence $s = \int \frac{r\, dx}{\sqrt{(r^2 - x^2)}} = r\,\text{arc}\left(\sin\frac{x}{r}\right) + C$, C being a constant.

As the integration is only to be made between $x = 0$ and $x = r$, we write

$$s = \int_0^r \frac{r\, dx}{\sqrt{(r^2 - x^2)}} = \left[r\,\text{arc}\left(\sin\frac{x}{r}\right) + C \right]_0^r;$$

proceeding then as explained in Example (1), p. 176, we get

$$s = r\,\text{arc}\left(\sin\frac{r}{r}\right) + C - r\,\text{arc}\left(\sin\frac{0}{r}\right) - C, \quad \text{or} \quad s = r \times \frac{\pi}{2},$$

since arc (sin 1) is 90° or $\frac{\pi}{2}$ and arc (sin 0) is zero, and the constant C disappears, as has been shown.

The length of the quadrant is therefore $\frac{\pi r}{2}$, and the length of the circumference, being four times this, is $4 \times \frac{\pi r}{2} = 2\pi r$.

Example 2.   Find the length of the arc AB between $x_1 = 2$ and $x_2 = 5$, in the circumference $x^2 + y^2 = 6^2$ (see Fig. 68).

Fig. 68.

Here, proceeding as in previous example,

$$s = \left[r \text{ arc sin} \left(\frac{x}{r}\right) + C \right]_{x_1}^{x_2} = \left[6 \text{ arc sin} \left(\frac{x}{6}\right) + C \right]_{2}^{5}$$

$$= 6 \left[\text{arc sin} \left(\frac{5}{6}\right) - \text{arc sin} \left(\frac{2}{6}\right) = 6(0 \cdot 9850 - 0 \cdot 3397) \right.$$

$$= 3 \cdot 8718 \text{ inches (the arcs being expressed in radians).}$$

It is always well to check results obtained by a new and yet unfamiliar method.   This is easy, for

$$\cos AOX = \tfrac{2}{6} = \tfrac{1}{3} \text{ and } \cos BOX = \tfrac{5}{6} ;$$

hence $AOX = 70° 32', BOX = 33° 34',$

and $\qquad AOX - BOX = AOB = 36° 58'$

$$= \frac{36 \cdot 9667}{57 \cdot 2958} \text{ radian} = 0 \cdot 6451 \text{ radian} = 3 \cdot 8706 \text{ inches},$$

the discrepancy being merely due to the fact that the last decimal in logarithmic and trigonometrical tables is only approximate.

Example 3. Find the length of an arc of the curve

$$y = \frac{a}{2} \left\{ \epsilon^{\frac{x}{a}} + \epsilon^{-\frac{x}{a}} \right\}$$

between $x = 0$ and $x = a$. (This curve is the *catenary*.)

$$y = \frac{a}{2} \epsilon^{\frac{x}{a}} + \frac{a}{2} \epsilon^{-\frac{x}{a}}, \quad \frac{dy}{dx} = \frac{1}{2} \left\{ \epsilon^{\frac{x}{a}} - \epsilon^{-\frac{x}{a}} \right\},$$

$$s = \int \sqrt{1 + \frac{1}{4} \left\{ \epsilon^{\frac{x}{a}} - \epsilon^{-\frac{x}{a}} \right\}^2} \, dx$$

$$= \frac{1}{2} \int \sqrt{4 + \epsilon^{\frac{2x}{a}} + \epsilon^{-\frac{2x}{a}} - 2\epsilon^{\frac{x}{a} - \frac{x}{a}}} \, dx.$$

Now

$$\epsilon^{\frac{x}{a} - \frac{x}{a}} = \epsilon^0 = 1, \text{ so that } s = \frac{1}{2} \int \sqrt{2 + \epsilon^{\frac{2x}{a}} + \epsilon^{-\frac{2x}{a}}} \, dx ;$$

we can replace 2 by $2 \times \epsilon^0 = 2 \times \epsilon^{\frac{x}{a} - \frac{x}{a}}$; then

$$s = \frac{1}{2} \int \sqrt{\epsilon^{\frac{2x}{a}} + 2\epsilon^{\frac{x}{a} - \frac{x}{a}} + \epsilon^{-\frac{2x}{a}}} \, dx$$

$$= \frac{1}{2} \int \sqrt{\left(\epsilon^{\frac{x}{a}} + \epsilon^{-\frac{x}{a}} \right)^2} \, dx = \frac{1}{2} \int \left(\epsilon^{\frac{x}{a}} + \epsilon^{-\frac{x}{a}} \right) dx$$

$$= \frac{1}{2} \int \epsilon^{\frac{x}{a}} \, dx + \frac{1}{2} \int \epsilon^{-\frac{x}{a}} \, dx = \frac{a}{2} \left[\epsilon^{\frac{x}{a}} - \epsilon^{-\frac{x}{a}} \right].$$

Here $\qquad s = \frac{a}{2} \left[\epsilon^{\frac{x}{a}} - \epsilon^{-\frac{x}{a}} \right]_0^a = \frac{a}{2} \left[\epsilon^1 - \epsilon^{-1} + 1 - 1 \right],$

and $\qquad s = \frac{a}{2} \left(\epsilon - \frac{1}{\epsilon} \right) = 1 \cdot 1752a.$

Example 4. A curve is such that the length of the tangent at any point P (see Fig. 69) from P to the intersection T of

FIG. 69.

the tangent with a fixed line AB is a constant length a. Find an expression for an arc of this curve—which is called the tractrix—and find the length, when $a=3$, between the ordinates $y=a$ and $y=1$.

We shall take the fixed line for the axis of x. The point D, with $DO=a$, is a point on the curve, which must be tangent to OD at D. We take OD as the axis of y; AB and OD are what are called axes of symmetry, that is, the curve is symmetrical about them; $PT=a$, $PN=y$, $ON=x$.

If we consider a small portion ds of the curve, at P, then $\sin \theta = \dfrac{dy}{ds} = -\dfrac{y}{a}$ (minus because the curve slopes *downwards* to the right, see p. 67).

Hence $\dfrac{ds}{dy} = -\dfrac{a}{y}$, $ds = -a\dfrac{dy}{y}$ and $s = -a\int \dfrac{dy}{y}$, that is,

$$s = -a \log_\epsilon y + C.$$

When $x=0$, $s=0$, $y=a$, so that $0 = -a\log_\epsilon a + C$, and $C = a\log_\epsilon a$.

It follows that $s = a \log_\epsilon a - a \log_\epsilon y = a \log_\epsilon \dfrac{a}{y}$.

When $a = 3$, s between $y = a$ and $y = 1$ is therefore

$$s = 3 \left[\log_\epsilon \frac{3}{y} \right]_1^3 = 3 \left(\log_\epsilon 1 - \log_\epsilon 3 \right) = 3 \times (0 - 1 \cdot 0986)$$

$$= -3 \cdot 296 \text{ or } 3 \cdot 296,$$

as the sign $-$ refers merely to the direction in which the length was measured, from D to P, or from P to D.

Note that this result has been obtained without a knowledge of the equation of the curve. This is sometimes possible. In order to get the length of an arc between two points given by their abscissae, however, it is necessary to know the equation of the curve ; this is easily obtained as follows :

$$\frac{dy}{dx} = - \tan \theta = - \frac{y}{\sqrt{a^2 - y^2}} \text{, since } PT = a \text{ ;}$$

hence $\qquad dx = - \dfrac{\sqrt{a^2 - y^2}\, dy}{y}, \quad \text{and} \quad x = - \displaystyle\int \frac{\sqrt{a^2 - y^2}\, dy}{y}$.

The integration will give us a relation between x and y, which is the equation of the curve.

To effect the integration, let $u^2 = a^2 - y^2$, then

$$2u\, du = -2y\, dy, \quad \text{or} \quad u\, du = -y\, dy.$$

$$\therefore\ x = \int \frac{u^2\, du}{y^2} = \int \frac{u^2\, du}{a^2 - u^2} = \int \frac{a^2 - (a^2 - u^2)}{a^2 - u^2}\, .\, du$$

$$= a^2 \int \frac{du}{a^2 - u^2} - \int du$$

$$= a^2 \cdot \frac{1}{2a} \log_\epsilon \frac{a + u}{a - u} - u + C \text{ (see pp. 193–4)}$$

$$= \tfrac{1}{2} a \log_\epsilon \frac{(a + u)(a + u)}{(a - u)(a + u)} - u + C$$

$$= a \log_\epsilon \frac{a + u}{\sqrt{a^2 - u^2}} - u + C.$$

We have then, finally,

$$x = a \log_\epsilon \frac{a + \sqrt{a^2 - y^2}}{y} - \sqrt{a^2 - y^2} + C.$$

When $x = 0$, $y = a$, so that $0 = a \log_\epsilon 1 - 0 + C$, and $C = 0$; the equation of the tractrix is therefore

$$x = a \log_\epsilon \frac{a + \sqrt{a^2 - y^2}}{y} - \sqrt{a^2 - y^2}.$$

If $a = 3$, as before, and if the length of the arc from $x = 0$ to $x = 1$ is required, it is not an easy matter to calculate the value of y corresponding to any given numerical value of x. It is, however, easy to find graphically an approximation as near the correct value as we desire, when we are given the value of a as follows :

Plot the graph, giving suitable values to y, say 3, 2, 1·5, 1. From this graph, find what values of y correspond to the two given values of x determining the arc, the length of which is needed, as accurately as the scale of the graph allows. For $x = 0$, $y = 3$ of course ; suppose that for $x = 1$ you find $y = 1·72$ on the graph. This is only approximate. Now plot again, on as large a scale as possible, taking only three values of y, 1·6, 1·7, 1·8. On this second graph, which is nearly, but not quite a straight line, you will be probably able to read any value of y correct to three places of decimals, and this is sufficient for our purpose. We find from the graph that $y = 1·723$ corresponds to $x = 1$. Then

$$s = 3 \left[\log_\epsilon \frac{3}{y} \right]_{x=0}^{x=1} = 3 \left[\log_\epsilon \frac{3}{y} \right]_3^{1·723}$$

$$= 3 \left(\log_\epsilon 1·741 - 0 \right) = 1·66.$$

If we wanted a more accurate value of y we could plot a third graph, taking for values of y 1·722, 1·723, 1·724, ... ; this would give us, correct to five places of decimals, the value of y corresponding to $x = 1$, and so on, till the required accuracy is reached.

Example 5.   Find the length of an arc of the logarithmic spiral $r = \epsilon^\theta$ between $\theta = 0$ and $\theta = 1$ radian.

Do you remember differentiating $y = \epsilon^x$? It is an easy one to remember, for it remains always the same whatever is done to it : $\dfrac{dy}{dx} = \epsilon^x$ (see p. 118).

Here, since $\qquad r = \epsilon^\theta, \quad \dfrac{dr}{d\theta} = \epsilon^\theta = r.$

If we reverse the progress and integrate $\displaystyle\int \epsilon^\theta \, d\theta$ we get back to $r + C$, the constant C being always introduced by such a process, as we have seen in Chap. XVII.

It follows that

$$s = \int \sqrt{\left[r^2 + \left(\frac{dr}{d\theta}\right)^2 \right]} \, d\theta = \int \sqrt{(r^2 + r^2)} \, d\theta$$

$$= \sqrt{2} \int r \, d\theta = \sqrt{2} \int \epsilon^\theta \, d\theta = \sqrt{2}(\epsilon^\theta + C).$$

Integrating between the two given values $\theta = 0$ and $\theta = 1$, we get

$$s = \int_0^1 \sqrt{\left[r^2 + \left(\frac{dr}{d\theta}\right)^2 \right]} \, d\theta = \left[\sqrt{2}(\epsilon^\theta + C) \right]_0^1$$

$$= \sqrt{2}\epsilon^1 - \sqrt{2}\epsilon^0 = \sqrt{2}(\epsilon - 1)$$

$$= 1{\cdot}41 \times 1{\cdot}718 = 2{\cdot}43 \text{ inches.}$$

Example 6.   Find the length of an arc of the logarithmic spiral $r = \epsilon^\theta$ between $\theta = 0$ and $\theta = \theta_1$.

As we have just seen,

$$s = \sqrt{2} \int_0^{\theta_1} \epsilon^\theta \, d\theta = \sqrt{2} \left[\epsilon^{\theta_1} - \epsilon^0 \right] = \sqrt{2} \left(\epsilon^{\theta_1} - 1 \right).$$

Example 7. As a last example let us work fully a case leading to a typical integration which will be found useful for several of the exercises found at the end of this chapter. Let us find the expression for the length of an arc of the curve $y = \dfrac{a}{2} x^2 + 3$.

$$\frac{dy}{dx} = ax, \quad s = \int \sqrt{1 + a^2 x^2}\, dx.$$

To work out this integral, let $ax = \sinh z$ (see p. 144), then $a\, dx = \cosh z\, dz$, and $1 + a^2 x^2 = 1 + \sinh^2 z = \cosh^2 z$;

$$\therefore\ s = \frac{1}{a} \int \cosh^2 z\, dz = \frac{1}{4a} \int (\epsilon^{2z} + 2 + \epsilon^{-2z})\, dz$$

$$= \frac{1}{4a} [\tfrac{1}{2}\epsilon^{2z} + 2z - \tfrac{1}{2}\epsilon^{-2z}] = \frac{1}{8a} [\, (\epsilon^z)^2 - (\epsilon^{-z})^2 + 4z]$$

$$= \frac{1}{8a} (\epsilon^z - \epsilon^{-z})(\epsilon^z + \epsilon^{-z}) + \frac{z}{2a}$$

$$= \frac{1}{2a} (\sinh z \cosh z + z) = \frac{1}{2a} (ax\sqrt{1 + a^2 x^2} + z).$$

To turn z back into terms of x, we have

$$ax = \sinh z = \tfrac{1}{2} (\epsilon^z - \epsilon^{-z}).$$

Multiply out by $2\epsilon^z$,

$$2ax\epsilon^z = \epsilon^{2z} - 1,$$

or $$(\epsilon^z)^2 - 2ax\,(\epsilon^z) - 1 = 0.$$

This is a quadratic equation in ϵ^z, and taking the positive root :

$$\epsilon^z = \tfrac{1}{2} (2ax + \sqrt{4a^2 x^2 + 4}) = ax + \sqrt{1 + a^2 x^2}.$$

Taking natural logarithms :

$$z = \log_\epsilon (ax + \sqrt{1 + a^2 x^2}).$$

Hence, the integral becomes finally :

$$s = \int \sqrt{1 + a^2 x^2}\, dx = \frac{x}{2} \sqrt{1 + a^2 x^2} + \frac{1}{2a} \log_\epsilon (ax + \sqrt{1 + a^2 x^2}),$$

From several of the foregoing examples, some very important integrals and relations have been worked out. As these are of great use in solving many other problems, it will be an advantage to collect them here for future reference.

Inverse Hyperbolic Functions

If $x = \sinh z$, z is written inversely as $\sinh^{-1}x$;

and $\qquad z = \sinh^{-1}x = \log_\epsilon(x + \sqrt{x^2 + 1})$.   (See p. 232.)

Similarly, if $x = \cosh z$,

$$z = \cosh^{-1}x = \log_\epsilon(x + \sqrt{x^2 - 1}).$$

Irrational Quadratic Integrals

(i) $\displaystyle\int \frac{\sqrt{a^2 - x^2}}{x}\,dx = \sqrt{a^2 - x^2} - a\log_\epsilon\frac{a + \sqrt{a^2 - x^2}}{x} + C.$

(ii) $\displaystyle\int \sqrt{a^2 + x^2}\,dx = \tfrac{1}{2}x\sqrt{a^2 + x^2} + \tfrac{1}{2}a^2\log_\epsilon(x + \sqrt{a^2 + x^2}) + C.$

To these may be added :

(iii) $\displaystyle\int \frac{dx}{\sqrt{a^2 + x^2}} = \log_\epsilon(x + \sqrt{a^2 + x^2}) + C.$

For, if $x = a\sinh u$, $dx = a\cosh u\,du$, and

$$\int \frac{dx}{\sqrt{a^2 + x^2}} = \int du = u + C' = \sinh^{-1}\frac{x}{a} + C'$$

$$= \log_\epsilon\frac{x + \sqrt{a^2 + x^2}}{a} + C'$$

$$= \log_\epsilon(x + \sqrt{a^2 + x^2}) + C.$$

See also (5) on p. 190, and pp. 193–4.

You ought now to be able to attempt with success the following exercises. You will find it interesting as well as instructive to plot the curves and verify your results by measurement where possible.

EXERCISES XXII

(See page 250 for Answers)

(1) Find the length of the line $y = 3x + 2$ between the two points for which $x = 1$ and $x = 4$.

(2) Find the length of the line $y = ax + b$ between the two points for which $x = -1$ and $x = a^2$.

(3) Find the length of the curve $y = \frac{2}{3}x^{\frac{3}{2}}$ between the two points for which $x = 0$ and $x = 1$.

(4) Find the length of the curve $y = x^2$ between the two points for which $x = 0$ and $x = 2$.

(5) Find the length of the curve $y = mx^2$ between the two points for which $x = 0$ and $x = \dfrac{1}{2m}$.

(6) Find the length of the curve $x = a \cos \theta$ and $y = a \sin \theta$ between $\theta = \theta_1$ and $\theta = \theta_2$.

(7) Find the length of the curve $r = a \sec \theta$.

(8) Find the length of the arc of the curve $y^2 = 4ax$ between $x = 0$ and $x = a$.

(9) Find the length of the arc of the curve $y = x\left(\dfrac{x}{2} - 1\right)$ between $x = 0$ and $x = 4$.

(10) Find the length of the arc of the curve $y = \epsilon^x$ between $x = 0$ and $x = 1$.

(*Note.* This curve is in rectangular coordinates, and is not the same curve as the logarithmic spiral $r = \epsilon^\theta$ which is in polar coordinates. The two equations are similar, but the curves are quite different.)

(11) A curve is such that the coordinates of a point on it are $x = a(\theta - \sin \theta)$ and $y = a(1 - \cos \theta)$, θ being a certain angle which varies between 0 and 2π. Find the length of the curve. (It is called a *cycloid*.)

(12) Find the length of an arc of the curve $y = \log_e \sec x$ between $x = 0$ and $x = \dfrac{\pi}{4}$ radians.

(13) Find the expression for the length of an arc of the curve $y^2 = \dfrac{x^3}{a}$.

(14) Find the length of the curve $y^2 = 8x^3$ between the two points for which $x = 1$ and $x = 2$.

(15) Find the length of the curve $y^{\frac{2}{3}} + x^{\frac{2}{3}} = a^{\frac{2}{3}}$ between $x = 0$ and $x = a$.

(16) Find the length of the curve $r = a(1 - \cos \theta)$ between $\theta = 0$ and $\theta = \pi$.

———————

You have now been personally conducted over the frontiers into the enchanted land. And in order that you may have a handy reference to the principal results, the author, in bidding you farewell, begs to present you with a passport in the shape of a convenient collection of standard forms (see pp. 238-9). In the middle column are set down a number of the functions which most commonly occur. The results of differentiating them are set down on the left ; the results of integrating them are set down on the right. May you find them useful!

EPILOGUE AND APOLOGUE

It may be confidently assumed that when this tractate *Calculus Made Easy* falls into the hands of the professional mathematicians, they will (if not too lazy) rise up as one man, and damn it as being a thoroughly bad book. Of that there can be, from their point of view, no possible manner of doubt whatever. It commits several most grievous and deplorable errors.

First, it shows how ridiculously easy most of the operations of the calculus really are.

Secondly, it gives away so many trade secrets. By showing you that *what one fool can do, other fools can do also*, it lets you see that these mathematical swells, who pride themselves on having mastered such an awfully difficult subject as the calculus, have no such great reason to be puffed up. They like you to think how terribly difficult it is, and don't want that superstition to be rudely dissipated.

Thirdly, among the dreadful things they will say about " So Easy " is this : that there is an utter failure on the part of the author to demonstrate with rigid and satisfactory completeness the validity of sundry methods which he has presented in simple fashion, and has even *dared to use* in solving problems! But why should he not? You don't forbid the use of a watch to every person who does not know how to make one? You don't object to the musician playing on a violin that he has not himself constructed. You don't teach the rules of syntax to children until they have already become fluent in the *use* of speech. It would be equally absurd to require general rigid demonstrations to be expounded to beginners in the calculus.

One other thing will the professed mathematicians say about this thoroughly bad and vicious book : that the reason why it is *so easy* is because the author has left out all the things that are really difficult. And the ghastly fact about this accusation is that—*it is true!* That is, indeed, why the book has been written—written for the legion of innocents who have hitherto been deterred from acquiring the elements of the calculus by the stupid way in which its teaching is almost always presented. Any subject can be made repulsive by presenting it bristling with difficulties. The aim of this book is to enable beginners to learn its language, to acquire familiarity with its endearing simplicities, and to grasp its powerful methods of solving problems, without being compelled to toil through the intricate out-of-the-way (and mostly irrelevant) mathematical gymnastics so dear to the unpractical mathematician.

There are amongst young engineers a number on whose ears the adage that *what one fool can do, another can,* may fall with a familiar sound. They are earnestly requested not to give the author away, nor to tell the mathematicians what a fool he really is.

TABLE OF STANDARD FORMS

$\dfrac{dy}{dx}\longleftarrow$	$\longmapsto\ y\ \longrightarrow$	$\longmapsto\displaystyle\int y\,dx$
Algebraic		
1	x	$\frac{1}{2}x^2 + C$
0	a	$ax + C$
1	$x \pm a$	$\frac{1}{2}x^2 \pm ax + C$
a	ax	$\frac{1}{2}ax^2 + C$
$2x$	x^2	$\frac{1}{3}x^3 + C$
nx^{n-1}	x^n	$\dfrac{1}{n+1}x^{n+1} + C$
$-x^{-2}$	x^{-1}	$\log_\epsilon x + C$
$\dfrac{du}{dx} \pm \dfrac{dv}{dx} \pm \dfrac{dw}{dx}$	$u \pm v \pm w$	$\displaystyle\int u\,dx \pm \int v\,dx \pm \int w\,dx$
$u\dfrac{dv}{dx} + v\dfrac{du}{dx}$	uv	Put $v = dy$ and integrate by parts
$\dfrac{v\dfrac{du}{dx} - u\dfrac{dv}{dx}}{v^2}$	$\dfrac{u}{v}$	No general form known
$\dfrac{du}{dx}$	u	$\displaystyle\int u\,dx = ux - \int x\,du + C$
Exponential and Logarithmic		
ϵ^x	ϵ^x	$\epsilon^x + C$
x^{-1}	$\log_\epsilon x$	$x(\log_\epsilon x - 1) + C$
$0.4343 \times x^{-1}$	$\log_{10} x$	$0.4343x(\log_\epsilon x - 1) + C$
$a^x \log_\epsilon a$	a^x .	$\dfrac{a^x}{\log_\epsilon a} + C$
Trigonometrical		
$\cos x$	$\sin x$	$-\cos x + C$
$-\sin x$	$\cos x$	$\sin x + C$
$\sec^2 x$	$\tan x$	$-\log_\epsilon \cos x + C$
Circular (Inverse)		
$\dfrac{1}{\sqrt{(1-x^2)}}$	$\text{arc}\sin x$	$x \cdot \text{arc}\sin x + \sqrt{1-x^2} + C$
$-\dfrac{1}{\sqrt{(1-x^2)}}$	$\text{arc}\cos x$	$x \cdot \text{arc}\cos x - \sqrt{1-x^2} + C$
$\dfrac{1}{1+x^2}$	$\text{arc}\tan x$	$x \cdot \text{arc}\tan x - \frac{1}{2}\log_\epsilon(1+x^2) + C$

$\dfrac{dy}{dx}\ \longleftarrow$	$\longleftarrow\ \ y\ \ \longrightarrow$	$\longrightarrow \quad \displaystyle\int y\,dx$
	Hyperbolic	
$\cosh x$	$\sinh x$	$\cosh x + C$
$\sinh x$	$\cosh x$	$\sinh x + C$
$\operatorname{sech}^2 x$	$\tanh x$	$\log_\epsilon \cosh x + C$
	Miscellaneous	
$-\dfrac{1}{(x+a)^2}$	$\dfrac{1}{x+a}$	$\log_\epsilon (x+a) + C$
$-\dfrac{x}{(a^2+x^2)^{\frac{3}{2}}}$	$\dfrac{1}{\sqrt{a^2+x^2}}$	$\log_\epsilon (x+\sqrt{a^2+x^2}) + C$
$\mp\dfrac{b}{(a\pm bx)^2}$	$\dfrac{1}{a\pm bx}$	$\pm\dfrac{1}{b}\log_\epsilon (a\pm bx) + C$
$\dfrac{-3a^2x}{(a^2+x^2)^{\frac{5}{2}}}$	$\dfrac{a^2}{(a^2+x^2)^{\frac{3}{2}}}$	$\dfrac{x}{\sqrt{a^2+x^2}} + C$
$a\cdot\cos ax$	$\sin ax$	$-\dfrac{1}{a}\cos ax + C$
$-a\cdot\sin ax$	$\cos ax$	$\dfrac{1}{a}\sin ax + C$
$a\cdot\sec^2 ax$	$\tan ax$	$-\dfrac{1}{a}\log_\epsilon \cos ax + C$
$\sin 2x$	$\sin^2 x$	$\dfrac{x}{2}-\dfrac{\sin 2x}{4} + C$
$-\sin 2x$	$\cos^2 x$	$\dfrac{x}{2}+\dfrac{\sin 2x}{4} + C$
$n\cdot\sin^{n-1}x\cdot\cos x$	$\sin^n x$	$-\dfrac{\cos x}{n}\sin^{n-1}x+\dfrac{n-1}{n}\displaystyle\int\sin^{n-2}x\,dx + C$
$-\dfrac{\cos x}{\sin^2 x}$	$\dfrac{1}{\sin x}$	$\log_\epsilon \tan\dfrac{x}{2} + C$
$-\dfrac{\sin 2x}{\sin^4 x}$	$\dfrac{1}{\sin^2 x}$	$-\cotan x + C$
$\dfrac{\sin^2 x - \cos^2 x}{\sin^2 x\cdot\cos^2 x}$	$\dfrac{1}{\sin x\cdot\cos x}$	$\log_\epsilon \tan x + C$
$n\cdot\sin mx\cdot\cos nx + m\cdot\sin nx\cdot\cos mx$	$\sin mx\cdot\sin nx$	$\tfrac{1}{2}\cos(m-n)x - \tfrac{1}{2}\cos(m+n)x + C$
$a\cdot\sin 2ax$	$\sin^2 ax$	$\dfrac{x}{2}-\dfrac{\sin 2ax}{4a} + C$
$-a\cdot\sin 2ax$	$\cos^2 ax$	$\dfrac{x}{2}+\dfrac{\sin 2ax}{4a} + C$

239

ANSWERS

Exercises I. (p. 21.)

(1) $\dfrac{dy}{dx} = 13x^{12}$. (2) $\dfrac{dy}{dx} = -\dfrac{3}{2}\,x^{-\frac{5}{2}}$. (3) $\dfrac{dy}{dx} = 2ax^{2a-1}$.

(4) $\dfrac{du}{dt} = 2\cdot 4t^{1\cdot4}$. (5) $\dfrac{dz}{du} = \dfrac{1}{3}\,u^{-\frac{2}{3}}$. (6) $\dfrac{dy}{dx} = -\dfrac{5}{3}\,x^{-\frac{8}{3}}$.

(7) $\dfrac{du}{dx} = -\dfrac{8}{5}\,x^{-1\frac{3}{5}}$. (8) $\dfrac{dy}{dx} = 2ax^{a-1}$.

(9) $\dfrac{dy}{dx} = \dfrac{3}{q}\,x^{\frac{3-q}{q}}$. (10) $\dfrac{dy}{dx} = -\dfrac{m}{n}\,x^{-\frac{m+n}{n}}$.

Exercises II. (p. 28.)

(1) $\dfrac{dy}{dx} = 3ax^2$. (2) $\dfrac{dy}{dx} = 13 \times \tfrac{3}{2}x^{\frac{1}{2}}$. (3) $\dfrac{dy}{dx} = 6x^{-\frac{1}{2}}$.

(4) $\dfrac{dy}{dx} = \dfrac{1}{2}\,c^{\frac{1}{2}}x^{-\frac{1}{2}}$. (5) $\dfrac{du}{dz} = \dfrac{an}{c}\,z^{n-1}$. (6) $\dfrac{dy}{dt} = 2\cdot 36t$.

(7) $\dfrac{dl_t}{dt} = 0\cdot000012 \times l_0$.

(8) $\dfrac{dc}{dV} = abV^{b-1}$, $0\cdot98$, $3\cdot00$ and $7\cdot47$ candle power per volt respectively.

(9) $\dfrac{dn}{dD} = -\dfrac{1}{LD^2}\sqrt{\dfrac{gT}{\pi\sigma}}$, $\dfrac{dn}{dL} = -\dfrac{1}{DL^2}\sqrt{\dfrac{gT}{\pi\sigma}}$,

$\dfrac{dn}{d\sigma} = -\dfrac{1}{2DL}\sqrt{\dfrac{gT}{\pi\sigma^3}}$, $\dfrac{dn}{dT} = \dfrac{1}{2DL}\sqrt{\dfrac{g}{\pi\sigma T}}$.

(10) $\dfrac{\text{Rate of change of } P \text{ when } t \text{ varies}}{\text{Rate of change of } P \text{ when } D \text{ varies}} = -\dfrac{D}{t}$.

(11) 2π, $2\pi r$, πl, $\tfrac{2}{3}\pi rh$, $8\pi r$, $4\pi r^2$. (12) $\dfrac{dD}{dT} = \dfrac{0\cdot000012 l_t}{\pi}$.

Exercises III. (p. 40.)

(1) (a) $1 + x + \dfrac{x^2}{2} + \dfrac{x^3}{6} + \dfrac{x^4}{24} + \ldots$. (b) $2ax + b$. (c) $2x + 2a$.

(d) $3x^2 + 6ax + 3a^2$.

(2) $\dfrac{dw}{dt} = a - bt.$

(3) $\dfrac{dy}{dx} = 2x.$

(4) $14110x^4 - 65404x^3 - 2244x^2 + 8192x + 1379.$

(5) $\dfrac{dx}{dy} = 2y + 8.$

(6) $185 \cdot 9022654x^2 + 154 \cdot 36334.$

(7) $\dfrac{-5}{(3x+2)^2}.$

(8) $\dfrac{6x^4 + 6x^3 + 9x^2}{(1 + x + 2x^2)^2}.$

(9) $\dfrac{ad - bc}{(cx + d)^2}.$

(10) $\dfrac{anx^{-n-1} + bnx^{n-1} + 2nx^{-1}}{(x^{-n} + b)^2}.$

(11) $b + 2ct.$

(12) $R_0(a + 2bt),\ R_0\left(a + \dfrac{b}{2\sqrt{t}}\right),\ -\dfrac{R_0(a + 2bt)}{(1 + at + bt^2)^2}$ or $-\dfrac{R^2(a + 2bt)}{R_0^2}.$

(13) $1 \cdot 4340(0 \cdot 000014t - 0 \cdot 001024),\ -0 \cdot 00117,\ -0 \cdot 00107,\ -0 \cdot 00097.$

(14) $(a)\ \dfrac{dE}{dl} = b + \dfrac{k}{i},\ \ (b)\ \dfrac{dE}{di} = -\dfrac{c + kl}{i^2}.$

Exercises IV. (p. 44.)

(1) $17 + 24x$; 24.

(2) $\dfrac{x^2 + 2ax - a}{(x + a)^2}$; $\dfrac{2a(a + 1)}{(x + a)^3}.$

(3) $1 + x + \dfrac{x^2}{1 \times 2} + \dfrac{x^3}{1 \times 2 \times 3}$; $1 + x + \dfrac{x^2}{1 \times 2}.$

(4) (*Exercises III*, p. 40) :

    (1) $(a)\ \dfrac{d^2u}{dx^2} = \dfrac{d^3u}{dx^3} = 1 + x + \frac{1}{2}x^2 + \frac{1}{6}x^3 + \ldots .$ $(b)\ 2a,\ 0.$

    $(c)\ 2,\ 0.$

    $(d)\ 6x + 6a,\ 6.$

    (2) $-b,\ 0.$

(3) $2,\ 0.$

    (4) $56440x^3 - 196212x^2 - 4488x + 8192.$ $169320x^2 - 392424x - 4488.$

    (5) $2,\ 0.$

(6) $371 \cdot 80453x,\ 371 \cdot 80453.$

    (7) $\dfrac{30}{(3x+2)^3},\ \ -\dfrac{270}{(3x+2)^4}.$

    (*Examples*, p. 35) :

    (1) $\dfrac{6a}{b^2}\,x,\ \dfrac{6a}{b^2}.$

(2) $\dfrac{3a\sqrt{b}}{2\sqrt{x}} - \dfrac{6b\sqrt[3]{a}}{x^3},\ \dfrac{18b\sqrt[3]{a}}{x^4} - \dfrac{3a\sqrt{b}}{4\sqrt{x^3}}.$

    (3) $\dfrac{2}{\sqrt[3]{\theta^8}} - \dfrac{1 \cdot 056}{\sqrt[5]{\theta^{11}}},\ \dfrac{2 \cdot 3232}{\sqrt[5]{\theta^{16}}} - \dfrac{16}{3\sqrt[3]{\theta^{11}}}.$

    (4) $810t^4 - 648t^3 + 479 \cdot 52t^2 - 139 \cdot 968t + 26 \cdot 64.$

        $3240t^3 - 1944t^2 + 959 \cdot 04t - 139 \cdot 968.$

(5) $12x + 2$, 12.
(6) $6x^2 - 9x$, $12x - 9$.

(7) $\frac{3}{4}\left(\frac{1}{\sqrt{\theta}} + \frac{1}{\sqrt{\theta^5}}\right) + \frac{1}{4}\left(\frac{15}{\sqrt{\theta^7}} - \frac{1}{\sqrt{\theta^3}}\right)$. $\frac{3}{8}\left(\frac{1}{\sqrt{\theta^5}} - \frac{1}{\sqrt{\theta^3}}\right) - \frac{15}{8}\left(\frac{7}{\sqrt{\theta^9}} + \frac{1}{\sqrt{\theta^7}}\right)$.

Exercises V. (p. 55.)

(2) 64; $147 \cdot 2$; and $0 \cdot 32$ feet per second.

(3) $\ddot{x} = a - gt$; $\ddot{x} = -g$.   (4) $45 \cdot 1$ feet per second.

(5) $12 \cdot 4$ feet per second per second. Yes.

(6) Angular velocity $= 11 \cdot 2$ radians per second; angular acceleration $= 9 \cdot 6$ radians per second per second.

(7) $v = 20 \cdot 4t^2 - 10 \cdot 8$. $a = 40 \cdot 8t$. $172 \cdot 8$ in./sec., $122 \cdot 4$ in./sec.²

(8) $v = \dfrac{1}{30 \sqrt[3]{(t - 125)^2}}$, $a = -\dfrac{1}{45\sqrt[3]{(t-125)^5}}$.

(9) $v = 0 \cdot 8 - \dfrac{8t}{(4 + t^2)^2}$, $a = \dfrac{24t^2 - 32}{(4 + t^2)^3}$, $0 \cdot 7926$ and $0 \cdot 00211$.

(10) $n = 2$, $n = 11$.

Exercises VI. (p. 62.)

(1) $\dfrac{x}{\sqrt{x^2 + 1}}$.
(2) $\dfrac{x}{\sqrt{x^2 + a^2}}$.
(3) $-\dfrac{1}{2\sqrt{(a + x)^3}}$.

(4) $\dfrac{ax}{\sqrt{(a - x^2)^3}}$.
(5) $\dfrac{2a^2 - x^2}{x^3\sqrt{x^2 - a^2}}$.

(6) $\dfrac{\frac{3}{2}x^2[\frac{5}{6}x(x^3 + a) - (x^4 + a)]}{(x^4 + a)^{\frac{2}{3}}(x^3 + a)^{\frac{3}{2}}}$.
(7) $\dfrac{2a(x - a)}{(x + a)^3}$.

(8) $\frac{5}{2}y^3$.
(9) $\dfrac{1}{(1 - \theta)\sqrt{1 - \theta^2}}$.

Exercises VII. (p. 64.)

(1) $\dfrac{dw}{dx} = -\dfrac{3x^2(3 + 3x^3)}{27(\frac{1}{2}x^3 + \frac{1}{4}x^6)^3}$.

(2) $\dfrac{dv}{dx} = -\dfrac{12x}{\sqrt{1 + \sqrt{2} + 3x^2}(\sqrt{3} + 4\sqrt{1 + \sqrt{2} + 3x^2})^2}$.

(3) $\dfrac{du}{dx} = -\dfrac{x^2(\sqrt{3} + x^3)}{\sqrt{\left[1 + \left(1 + \frac{x^3}{\sqrt{3}}\right)^2\right]^3}}$.

(5) $\dfrac{dx}{d\theta}=a(1-\cos\theta)=2a\sin^2\tfrac12\theta,$

$\dfrac{dy}{d\theta}=a\sin\theta=2a\sin\tfrac12\theta\cos\tfrac12\theta;\ \dfrac{dy}{dx}=\cot\tfrac12\theta.$

(6) $\dfrac{dx}{d\theta}=-3a\cos^2\theta\sin\theta,\ \dfrac{dy}{d\theta}=3a\sin^2\theta\cos\theta;\ \dfrac{dy}{dx}=-\tan\theta.$

(7) $\dfrac{dy}{dx}=2x\cot(x^2-a^2).$

(8) Write $x=u-y$; find $\dfrac{dy}{du},\ \dfrac{du}{dx}$ and then $\dfrac{dy}{dx}.$

Exercises VIII. (p. 76.)

(2) $1\cdot44.$

(4) $\dfrac{dy}{dx}=3x^2+3$; and the numerical values are : **3, $3\tfrac34$, 6, and 15.**

(5) $\pm\sqrt2.$

(6) $\dfrac{dy}{dx}=-\dfrac49\dfrac{x}{y}.$ Slope is zero where $x=0$; and is $\mp\dfrac{1}{3\sqrt2}$ where **$x=1.$**

(7) $m=4,\ n=-3.$

(8) Intersections at $x=1,\ x=-3.$ Angles $153°\,26',\ 2°\,28'.$

(9) Intersection at $x=3\cdot57,\ y=3\cdot57.$ Angle $16°\,16'.$

(10) $x=\tfrac13,\ y=2\tfrac13,\ b=-\tfrac53.$

Exercises IX. (p. 91.)

(1) Min. : $x=0,y=0$; max. : $x=-2,y=-4.$

(2) $x=a.$ **(4)** $25\sqrt3$ square inches.

(5) $\dfrac{dy}{dx}=-\dfrac{10}{x^2}+\dfrac{10}{(8-x)^2}$; $x=4$; $y=5.$

(6) Max. for $x=-1$; min. for $x=1.$

(7) Join the middle points of the four sides.

(8) $r=\tfrac23R,\ r=\dfrac R2$, no max. **(9)** $r=R\sqrt{\dfrac23},\ r=\dfrac{R}{\sqrt2},\ r=0\cdot8506R.$

(10) At the rate of $\dfrac8r$ square feet per second.

(11) $r=\dfrac{R\sqrt8}{3}.$ **(12)** $n=\sqrt{\dfrac{NR}{r}}.$

Exercises X. (p. 98.)

(1) Max.: $x = -2\cdot19$, $y = 24\cdot19$; min.: $x = 1\cdot52$, $y = -1\cdot38$.

(2) $\dfrac{dy}{dx} = \dfrac{b}{a} - 2cx$; $\dfrac{d^2y}{dx^2} = -2c$; $x = \dfrac{b}{2ac}$ (a *maximum*).

(3) (a) One maximum and two minima.
   (b) One maximum. ($x = 0$; other points unreal.)

(4) Min.: $x = 1\cdot71$, $y = 6\cdot14$.   (5) Max.: $x = -\cdot5$, $y = 4$.

(6) Max.: $x = 1\cdot414$, $y = 1\cdot7675$. Min.: $x = -1\cdot414$, $y = -1\cdot7675$.

(7) Max.: $x = -3\cdot565$, $y = 2\cdot12$. Min.: $x = +3\cdot565$, $y = 7\cdot88$.

(8) $0\cdot4N$, $0\cdot6N$.   (9) $x = \sqrt{\dfrac{a}{c}}$.

(10) Speed 8·66 nautical miles per hour. Time taken 115·47 hours. Minimum cost £112 12s.

(11) Max. and min. for $x = 7\cdot5$, $y = \pm5\cdot414$. See example no. 10, pp. 61–2.)

(12) Min.: $x = \frac{1}{2}$, $y = 0\cdot25$; max.: $x = -\frac{1}{3}$, $y = 1\cdot408$.

Exercises XI. (p. 107.)

(1) $\dfrac{2}{x-3} + \dfrac{1}{x+4}$.

(2) $\dfrac{1}{x-1} + \dfrac{2}{x-2}$.

(3) $\dfrac{2}{x-3} + \dfrac{1}{x+4}$.

(4) $\dfrac{5}{x-4} - \dfrac{4}{x-3}$.

(5) $\dfrac{19}{13(2x+3)} - \dfrac{22}{13(3x-2)}$.

(6) $\dfrac{2}{x-2} + \dfrac{4}{x-3} - \dfrac{5}{x-4}$.

(7) $\dfrac{1}{6(x-1)} + \dfrac{11}{15(x+2)} + \dfrac{1}{10(x-3)}$.

(8) $\dfrac{7}{9(3x+1)} + \dfrac{71}{63(3x-2)} - \dfrac{5}{7(2x+1)}$.

(9) $\dfrac{1}{3(x-1)} + \dfrac{2x+1}{3(x^2+x+1)}$.

(10) $x + \dfrac{2}{3(x+1)} + \dfrac{1-2x}{3(x^2-x+1)}$.

(11) $\dfrac{3}{x+1} + \dfrac{2x+1}{x^2+x+1}$.

(12) $\dfrac{1}{x-1} - \dfrac{1}{x-2} + \dfrac{2}{(x-2)^2}$.

(13) $\dfrac{1}{4(x-1)} - \dfrac{1}{4(x+1)} + \dfrac{1}{2(x+1)^2}$.

(14) $\dfrac{4}{9(x-1)} - \dfrac{4}{9(x+2)} - \dfrac{1}{3(x+2)^2}$.

(15) $\dfrac{1}{x+2} - \dfrac{x-1}{x^2+x+1} - \dfrac{1}{(x^2+x+1)^2}$.

(16) $\dfrac{5}{x+4} - \dfrac{32}{(x+4)^2} + \dfrac{36}{(x+4)^3}$.

(17) $\dfrac{7}{9(3x-2)^2} + \dfrac{55}{9(3x-2)^3} + \dfrac{73}{9(3x-2)^4}$.

(18) $\dfrac{1}{6(x-2)} + \dfrac{1}{3(x-2)^2} - \dfrac{x}{6(x^2+2x+4)}$.

Exercises XII. (p. 127.)

(1) $ab(\epsilon^{ax} + \epsilon^{-ax})$.   **(2)** $2at + \dfrac{2}{t}$·   **(3)** $\log_\epsilon n$.   **(5)** npv^{n-1}.

(6) $\dfrac{n}{x}$·   **(7)** $\dfrac{3\epsilon^{-\frac{x}{x-1}}}{(x-1)^2}$·   **(8)** $6x\epsilon^{-5x} - 5(3x^2 + 1)\epsilon^{-5x}$.

(9) $\dfrac{ax^{a-1}}{x^a + a}$·   **(10)** $\dfrac{15x^2 + 12x\sqrt{x} - 1}{2\sqrt{x}}$·   **(11)** $\dfrac{1 - \log_\epsilon(x+3)}{(x+3)^2}$·

(12) $a^x(ax^{a-1} + x^a \log_\epsilon a)$.   **(14)** Min. : $y = 0.7$ for $x = 0.694$.

(15) $\dfrac{1+x}{x}$·   **(16)** $\dfrac{3}{x}(\log_\epsilon ax)^2$.

Exercises XIII. (p. 135.)

(1) Let $\dfrac{t}{T} = x$ ($\therefore$ $t = 8x$), and use the Table on page 132.

(2) $T = 34.627$; 159.46 minutes.

(3) Take $2t = x$; and use the Table on page 132.

(5) (a) $x^x(1 + \log_\epsilon x)$; (b) $2x(\epsilon^x)^x$; (c) $\epsilon^{x^x} \times x^x(1 + \log_\epsilon x)$.

(6) 0.14 second.   **(7)** (a) 1.642 ; (b) 15.58.

(8) $\mu = 0.00037$, $31^m \frac{1}{4}$.

(9) i is 63.4% of i_0, 221.55 kilometres.

(10) Working as accurately as possible with a table of four-figure logarithms, $k = 0.1339$, 0.1445, 0.1553, mean $= 0.1446$; percentage errors :—10.2%, practically nil, $+71.9\%$.

(11) Min. for $x = \dfrac{1}{\epsilon}$·   **(12)** Max. for $x = \epsilon$.   **(13)** Min. for $x = \log_\epsilon a$.

Exercises XIV. (p. 144.)

(1) (i) $\dfrac{dy}{d\theta} = A \cos\left(\theta - \dfrac{\pi}{2}\right)$;

   (ii) $\dfrac{dy}{d\theta} = 2 \sin\theta \cos\theta = \sin 2\theta$ and $\dfrac{dy}{d\theta} = 2\cos 2\theta$;

   (iii) $\dfrac{dy}{d\theta} = 3 \sin^2\theta \cos\theta$ and $\dfrac{dy}{d\theta} = 3\cos 3\theta$.

(2) $\theta = 45°$ or $\dfrac{\pi}{4}$ radians.   **(3)** $\dfrac{dy}{dt} = -n \sin 2\pi nt$.   **(4)** $a^x \log_\epsilon a \cos a^x$.

(5) $\dfrac{-\sin x}{\cos x} = -\tan x$.   **(6)** $18.2 \cos(x + 26°)$.

(7) The slope is $\dfrac{dy}{d\theta} = 100 \cos(\theta - 15°)$, which is a maximum when $(\theta - 15°) = 0$, or $\theta = 15°$; the value of the slope being then $= 100$. When $\theta = 75°$ the slope is

$$100 \cos(75° - 15°) = 100 \cos 60° = 100 \times \tfrac{1}{2} = 50.$$

(8) $\cos\theta \sin 2\theta + 2\cos 2\theta \sin\theta = 2\sin\theta(\cos^2\theta + \cos 2\theta)$
$$= 2\sin\theta(3\cos^2\theta - 1).$$

(9) $amn\theta^{n-1}\tan^{m-1}(\theta^n)\sec^2\theta^n.$

(10) $\epsilon^x(\sin^2 x + \sin 2x)$; $\epsilon^x(\sin^2 x + 2\sin 2x + 2\cos 2x).$

(11) (i) $\dfrac{dy}{dx} = \dfrac{ab}{(x+b)^2}$; (ii) $\dfrac{a}{b}\epsilon^{-\frac{x}{b}}$; (iii) $\dfrac{1}{90°} \times \dfrac{ab}{(b^2 + x^2)}$.

(12) (i) $\dfrac{dy}{dx} = \sec x \tan x$; (ii) $\dfrac{dy}{dx} = -\dfrac{1}{\sqrt{1-x^2}}$; (iii) $\dfrac{dy}{dx} = \dfrac{1}{1+x^2}$;

(iv) $\dfrac{dy}{dx} = \dfrac{1}{x\sqrt{x^2-1}}$; (v) $\dfrac{dy}{dx} = \dfrac{\sqrt{3\sec x}\,(3\sec^2 x - 1)}{2}$.

(13) $\dfrac{dy}{d\theta} = 4\cdot6\,(2\theta+3)^{1\cdot3}\cos(2\theta+3)^{2\cdot3}.$

(14) $\dfrac{dy}{d\theta} = 3\theta^2 + 3\cos(\theta+3) - \log_\epsilon 3\,(\cos\theta \times 3\sin\theta + 3^\theta).$

(15) $\theta = \cot\theta$; $\theta = \pm0\cdot86$; $y = \pm0\cdot56$; is max. for $+\theta$, min. for $-\theta$.

Exercises XV. (p. 150.)

(1) $x^3 - 6x^2y - 2y^2$; $\tfrac{1}{3} - 2x^3 - 4xy.$

(2) $2xyz + y^2z + z^2y + 2xy^2z^2$;
$2xyz + x^2z + xz^2 + 2x^2yz^2$;
$2xyz + x^2y + xy^2 + 2x^2y^2z.$

(3) $\dfrac{1}{r}\{(x-a)+(y-b)+(z-c)\} = \dfrac{(x+y+z)-(a+b+c)}{r}$; $\dfrac{2}{r}$.

(4) $dy = v\,u^{v-1}\,du + u^v \log_\epsilon u\,dv.$

(5) $dy = 3\sin v\,u^2\,du + u^3\cos v\,dv$,
$dy = u\,(\sin x)^{u-1}\cos x\,dx + (\sin x)^u \log_\epsilon \sin x\,du$,

$dy = \dfrac{1}{v}\dfrac{1}{u}\,du - \log_\epsilon u\dfrac{1}{v^2}\,dv.$

(7) Minimum for $x = y = -\tfrac{1}{2}.$

(8) (a) Length 2 feet, width = depth = 1 foot, vol. = 2 cubic feet.

(b) Radius $= \dfrac{2}{\pi}$ feet $= 7\cdot64$ in., length $= 2$ feet, vol. $= 2\cdot54.$

(9) All three parts equal; the product is maximum.

(10) Minimum $=\epsilon^2$ for $x=y=1$.   **(11)** Min. $=2\cdot307$ for $x=\frac{1}{2}$, $y=2$.

(12) Angle at apex $=90°$; equal sides $=$ length $=\sqrt[3]{2V}$.

Exercises XVI. (p. 158.)

(1) $1\frac{1}{3}$.   **(2)** $0\cdot6344$.   **(3)** $0\cdot2624$.

(4) (a) $y=\frac{1}{3}x^3+C$; (b) $y=\sin x+C$.   **(5)** $y=x^2+3x+C$.

Exercises XVII. (p. 170.)

(1) $\dfrac{4\sqrt{a}\,x^{\frac{3}{2}}}{3}+C$.   **(2)** $-\dfrac{1}{x^3}+C$.   **(3)** $\dfrac{x^4}{4a}+C$.

(4) $\frac{1}{3}x^3+ax+C$.   **(5)** $-2x^{-\frac{5}{2}}+C$.

(6) $x^4+x^3+x^2+x+C$.   **(7)** $\dfrac{ax^2}{4}+\dfrac{bx^3}{9}+\dfrac{cx^4}{16}+C$.

(8) $\dfrac{x^2+a}{x+a}=x-a+\dfrac{a^2+a}{x+a}$ by division. Therefore the answer is

$\frac{1}{2}x^2-ax+a(a+1)\log_\epsilon(x+a)+C$.   (See pp. 165–7.)

(9) $\dfrac{x^4}{4}+3x^3+\dfrac{27}{2}x^2+27x+C$.   **(10)** $\dfrac{x^3}{3}+\dfrac{2-a}{2}x^2-2ax+C$.

(11) $a^2(2x^{\frac{3}{2}}+\frac{9}{4}x^{\frac{4}{3}})+C$.   **(12)** $-\frac{1}{3}\cos\theta-\frac{1}{6}\theta+C$.   **(13)** $\frac{1}{2}\theta+\dfrac{\sin 2a\theta}{4a}+C$.

(14) $\frac{1}{2}\theta-\frac{1}{4}\sin 2\theta+C$.   **(15)** $\frac{1}{2}\theta-\dfrac{\sin 2a\theta}{4a}+C$.   **(16)** $\frac{1}{3}\epsilon^{3x}+C$.

(17) $\log_\epsilon(1+x)+C$.   **(18)** $-\log_\epsilon(1-x)+C$.

Exercises XVIII. (p. 186.)

(1) Area $=60$; mean ordinate $=10$.   **(2)** Area $=\frac{4}{3}a^{\frac{5}{2}}$.

(3) Area $=2$; mean ordinate $=2/\pi=0\cdot637$.

(4) Area $=1\cdot57$; mean ordinate $=0\cdot5$.   **(5)** $0\cdot572$, $0\cdot0476$.

(6) Volume $=\frac{1}{3}\pi r^2 h$.   **(7)** $1\cdot25$.   **(8)** $79\cdot6$.

(9) Volume $=4\cdot935$, from 0 to π.   **(10)** $a\log_\epsilon a$, $\dfrac{a}{a-1}\log_\epsilon a$.

(12) A.M. $=9\cdot5$; Q.M. $=10\cdot85$.

(13) Quadratic mean $=\dfrac{1}{\sqrt{2}}\sqrt{A_1{}^2+A_3{}^2}$; arithmetical mean $=0$.

The first involves the integral

$$\int (A_1{}^2\sin^2 x + 2A_1A_3\sin x\sin 3x + A_3{}^2\sin^2 3x)\,dx$$

which may be evaluated by putting $\sin^2 x=\tfrac12(1-\cos 2x)$, $\sin^2 3x=\tfrac12(1-\cos 6x)$ and $2\sin x\sin 3x=\cos 2x-\cos 4x$.

(14) Area is 62·6 square units.   Mean ordinate is 10·45.

(16) 436·3.   (This solid is pear-shaped.)

Exercises XIX.   (p. 194.)

(1) $\dfrac{x\sqrt{a^2-x^2}}{2}+\dfrac{a^2}{2}\arcsin\dfrac{x}{a}+C.$

(2) $\dfrac{x^2}{2}\,(\log_\epsilon x-\tfrac12)+C.$

(3) $\dfrac{x^{a+1}}{a+1}\left(\log_\epsilon x-\dfrac{1}{a+1}\right)+C.$

(4) $\sin\epsilon^x+C.$

(5) $\sin(\log_\epsilon x)+C.$

(6) $\epsilon^x(x^2-2x+2)+C.$

(7) $\dfrac{1}{a+1}(\log_\epsilon x)^{a+1}+C.$

(8) $\log_\epsilon(\log_\epsilon x)+C.$

(9) $2\log_\epsilon(x-1)+3\log_\epsilon(x+2)+C.$

(10) $\tfrac12\log_\epsilon(x-1)+\tfrac16\log_\epsilon(x-2)+\tfrac{3}{10}\log_\epsilon(x+3)+C.$

(11) $\dfrac{b}{2a}\log_\epsilon\dfrac{x-a}{x+a}+C.$

(12) $\log_\epsilon\dfrac{x^2-1}{x^2+1}+C.$

(13) $\tfrac14\log_\epsilon\dfrac{1+x}{1-x}+\tfrac12\arctan x+C.$

(14) $-\dfrac{\sqrt{a^2-b^2x^2}}{b^2}+C.$

Exercises.   XX   (p. 207.)

(1) $T=T_0\epsilon^{\mu\theta}.$

(2) $s=ut+\tfrac12at^2.$

(3) Multiplying out by ϵ^{2t} gives $\dfrac{d}{dt}(i\epsilon^{2t})=\epsilon^{2t}\sin 3t$, so that,

$$i\epsilon^{2t}=\int\epsilon^{2t}\sin 3t\,dt=\tfrac{1}{13}\epsilon^{2t}(2\sin 3t-3\cos 3t)+E$$

from p. 200.   Since $i=0$ when $t=0$, $E=\tfrac{3}{13}$; hence the solution becomes $i=\tfrac{1}{13}(2\sin 3t-3\cos 3t+3\epsilon^{-2t})$.

Exercises XXI. (p. 220.)

(1) $r = 2\sqrt{2}$, $x_1 = -2$, $y_1 = 3$.   **(2)** $r = 2\cdot 83$, $x_1 = 0$, $y_1 = 2$.

(3) $x = \pm 0\cdot 383$, $y = 0\cdot 147$.   **(4)** $r = \sqrt{2m}$, $x_1 = y_1 = 2\sqrt{m}$.

(5) $r = 2a$, $x_1 = 2a + 3x$, $y_1 = -\dfrac{2x^{\frac{3}{2}}}{a^{\frac{1}{2}}}$ when $x = 0$, $x_1 = 2a$, $y_1 = 0$.

(6) When $x = 0$, $r = y_1 = $ infinity, $x_1 = 0$.
When $x = +0\cdot 9$, $r = 3\cdot 36$, $x_1 = -2\cdot 21$, $y_1 = +2\cdot 01$.
When $x = -0\cdot 9$, $r = 3\cdot 36$, $x_1 = +2\cdot 21$, $y = -2\cdot 01$.

(7) When $x = 0$, $r = 1\cdot 41$, $x_1 = 1$, $y_1 = 3$.
When $x = 1$, $r = 1\cdot 41$, $x_1 = 0$, $y_1 = 3$.
Minimum $= 1\cdot 75$.

(8) For $x = -2$, $r = 112\cdot 3$, $x_1 = 109\cdot 8$, $y_1 = -17\cdot 2$.
For $x = 0$, $r = x_1 = y_1 = $ infinity.
For $x = 1$, $r = 1\cdot 86$, $x_1 = -0\cdot 67$, $y_1 = -0\cdot 17$.

(9) $x = -0\cdot 33$, $y = +1\cdot 07$.

(10) $r = 1$, $x = 2$, $y = 0$ for all points.   A circle.

(11) When $x = 0$, $r = 1\cdot 86$, $x_1 = 1\cdot 67$, $y_1 = 0\cdot 17$.
When $x = 1\cdot 5$, $r = 0\cdot 365$, $x_1 = 1\cdot 59$, $y_1 = 0\cdot 98$.
$x = 1$, $y = 1$ for zero curvature.

(12) When $\theta = \dfrac{\pi}{2}$, $r = 1$, $x_1 = \dfrac{\pi}{2}$, $y_1 = 0$.

When $\theta = \dfrac{\pi}{4}$, $r = 2\cdot 598$, $x_1 = 2\cdot 285$, $y_1 = -1\cdot 414$.

(14) When $\theta = 0$, $r = 1$, $x_1 = 0$, $y_1 = 0$.

When $\theta = \dfrac{\pi}{4}$, $r = 2\cdot 598$, $x_1 = -0\cdot 715$, $y_1 = -1\cdot 414$.

When $\theta = \dfrac{\pi}{2}$, $r = x_1 = y_1 = $ infinity.

(15) $r = \dfrac{(a^4 y^2 + b^4 x^2)^{\frac{3}{2}}}{a^4 b^4}$, when $x = 0$, $y = \pm b$, $r = \dfrac{a^2}{b}$, $x_1 = 0$, $y_1 = \pm \dfrac{b^2 - a^2}{b}$;
when $y = 0$, $x = \pm a$, $r = \dfrac{b^2}{a}$, $x_1 = \pm \dfrac{a^2 - b^2}{a}$, $y_1 = 0$.

(16) $r = 4a \sin \tfrac{1}{3}\theta$.

Exercises XXII. (p. 234.)

(1) $J = 9\cdot487.$ **(2)** $s = (1 + a^2)^{\frac{3}{2}}.$ **(3)** $s = 1\cdot22.$

(4) $s = \int_0^2 \sqrt{1 + 4x^2}\, dx = \left[\frac{x}{2}\sqrt{1 + 4x^2} + \frac{1}{4}\log_\epsilon(2x + \sqrt{1 + 4x^2}) \right]_0^2 = 4\cdot65.$

(5) $s = \dfrac{0\cdot57}{m}.$ **(6)** $s = a(\theta_2 - \theta_1).$ **(7)** $s = \sqrt{r^2 - a^2}.$

(8) $s = \int_0^x \sqrt{1 + \dfrac{a}{x}}\, dx$ and $s = a\sqrt{2} + a\log_\epsilon(1 + \sqrt{2}) = 2\cdot30a.$

(9) $s = \dfrac{x-1}{2}\sqrt{(x-1)^2 + 1} + \frac{1}{2}\log_\epsilon\{(x-1) + \sqrt{(x-1)^2 + 1}\}$ and $s = 6\cdot80.$

(10) $s = \int_1^\epsilon \dfrac{\sqrt{1 + y^2}}{y}\, dy.$ Put $u^2 = 1 + y^2$; this leads to
$$s = \sqrt{1 + y^2} + \log_\epsilon \frac{y}{1 + \sqrt{1 + y^2}} \quad \text{and} \quad s = 2\cdot00.$$

(11) $s = 4a \int_0^\pi \sin\dfrac{\theta}{2}\, d\theta$ and $s = 8a.$

(12) $s = \int_0^{\frac{1}{4}\pi} \sec x\, dx.$ Put $u = \sin x$; this leads to $s = \log_\epsilon(1 + \sqrt{2}) = 0\cdot8812.$

(13) $s = \dfrac{8a}{27}\left\{ \left(1 + \dfrac{9x}{4a}\right)^{\frac{3}{2}} - 1 \right\}.$

(14) $s = \int_1^2 \sqrt{1 + 18x}\, dx.$ Let $1 + 18x = z$, express s in terms of z and integrate between the values of z corresponding to $x = 1$ and $x = 2.$ $s = 5\cdot27.$

(15) $s = \dfrac{3a}{2}.$ **(16)** $4a.$

Every earnest student is exhorted to manufacture more examples for himself at every stage, so as to test his powers. When integrating he can always test his answer by differentiating it, to see whether he gets back the expression from which he started.